Eating Light
and Loving It!

Simple Recipes for Good Health

Collected by
FRANCES JOHNSON, R.D.N. and SHAUNA RATNER, R.D.N.

Macmillan Canada
Toronto

Canadian Cataloguing in Publication Data

Main entry under title:
Eating light and loving it!
ISBN 0-7715-7593-9

1. Low-fat diet – Recipes.   I. Johnson, Frances, 1953-   .
II. Ratner, Shauna, 1963-   .
RM237.7.E27 1999   641.5'638   C98-932514-8

   2 3 4 5   FP   01 02 00 99

Cover design: D. Hunter, FIZZZ Design Inc.

Cover photograph: Douglas Bradshaw Photography

This book is available at special discounts for bulk purchases by your group or organization for sales promotions, premiums, fundraising and seminars. For details, contact: Macmillan Canada, Special Sales Department, 29 Birch Avenue, Toronto, ON M4V 1E2. Tel: 416-963-8830.

We acknowledge the financial support of the Government of Canada through the Book Publishing Industry Development Program for our publishing activities.

Macmillan Canada
A Division of Canada Publishing Corporation
Toronto, Ontario, Canada

Printed in Canada

INTRODUCTION

It's difficult to believe that years have passed since we first conceived the idea of creating a cookbook for the Lipid Clinic – a cookbook with recipes and ideas from experts in low fat cooking, mainly the participants of the Lipid Clinic.

We feel that this cookbook and its recipes are destined to be well-used and enjoyed. They have survived many obstacles, including the closure of the hospital in which this all began! Each recipe in the book has been prepared and taste-tested by the staff of the Clinic, and any other lucky visitor who happened to join us during one of our "Lipid Lunches." After passing the taste test, the recipes were analyzed for nutritional content to ensure suitability for low fat eating. Minor adjustments were made to some recipes. The outcome, we hope, is a collection of wonderful low fat recipes that all people interested in healthy living can enjoy for many years to come.

So it is with anticipation of your healthy eating and culinary enjoyment that we say...*Bon appetit!*

Frances Johnson and Shauna Ratner

ACKNOWLEDGMENTS

There are countless people who are responsible for helping to make this book a reality. We must first acknowledge all the Lipid Clinic participants who unselfishly shared their favourite recipes with us. Those who prepare and fine tune low fat recipes daily are the real experts in low fat cooking. We are thankful to them, for it is their recipes which have really made this cookbook.

This cookbook would not have been possible without another group of very dedicated interested people. Despite busy schedules at both work and home, the taste testers took recipes home to prepare for all of us to evaluate the next day at the "Lipid Lunch." Many many thanks to Rosa Benjamin, Francois Bowden, Debbie DeAngelis, Ruth Grierson, Gail James, Linda Peritz, Hannelore Vannetta, Linda Vicic, Angie Lim, and Yvonne Wallace for their precious time and efforts. A special thanks to Hannelore for all her help when we were unable to be there on time.

We are grateful to Dr. Jiri Frohlich and the other physicians in the Clinic for their support and encouragement. We are thankful to Veiko Tutti of Merck Frosst for his interest in our book and Merck Frosst Canada Inc. who provided support for our cookbook venture.

Finally, there are so many others who in their own ways have helped us to put this book together, and we must express our gratitude to them all.

PREFACE

Dear Reader:

You may ask the question "why another healthy cookbook?" In the minds of many people, a "healthy cookbook" is synonymous with a compilation of rather unappetizing recipes of dishes which turn our stomach and literally make us lean and mean because of the ill disposition following an unsatisfying meal.

Well then, let me assure you that this is not what we have done with this particular book. Think of the old joke "why didn't Marx try communism on dogs before suggesting it for people?" The Lipid Clinic crew, led by our intrepid dietitians, Frances Johnson and Shauna Ratner have cooked and savored every single one of the recipes. We prepared the dishes the day before and met at lunch where we tasted the various creations. We then rated them according to their appeal in appearance, taste, texture and general satisfaction. Not only did we all survive these exercises, but actually enjoyed them very much. It is interesting to note that in our fairly culturally diverse group, there was always almost unanimous agreement as to the best dish of the day.

Only the best dishes have been chosen for this cookbook. I admit that diet is not the be all and end all of a happy and healthy life, however, it certainly plays a very significant part. After all, "you are what you eat" as the old saying goes.

We hope that following the recipes in this book will make you happy, healthy and wise!

Bon Appetit!

Jiri Frohlich, MD, FRCPC
Director, Lipid Clinic

TABLE OF CONTENTS

EATING LIGHT AND LOVING IT...

Eating light means:

- less meat and more legumes
- small portions of lean meats, poultry and fish
- skim milk dairy products
- plenty of fruits and vegetables
- lots of whole grain foods
- very little extra fat such as margarine, vegetable oils and mayonnaise

So how much fat is too much fat?

- Total fat eaten should be no more than 30% of the calories eaten in one day. This translates into eating no more than 50 to 80 grams of fat per day. Remember, this is the **MOST** fat you should eat in one day.

- Fat is found in almost all foods, but in different amounts. Use this chart to get an idea of how much fat is in some foods.

FOOD ITEM	FAT { g }
lean red meat 3 oz/90 g	10
sausage 3 oz/90 g	30
poultry, no skin 3 oz/90 g	5
fish, e.g. sole, tuna 3 oz/90 g	1
skim milk 1 cup/250 mL	trace
whole milk 1 cup/250 mL	9
whipping cream 1 cup/250 mL	88
cheddar cheese 1 oz/30 g	10
2% cottage cheese 1/2 cup/125 mL	3
margarine 1 tbsp/15 mL	11
oil 1 tbsp/15 mL	14
mayonnaise 1 tbsp/15 mL	11
peanut butter 1 tbsp/15 mL	8
nuts, seeds 1/2 cup/125 mL	37
most fruits, vegetables, grains, pasta, bread, cereals (1 serving)	less than 2
pretzels, plain popcorn (1 serving)	less than 2
chips 10	7
chocolate 1 oz/30 g	10

HEALTHY BEGINNINGS

Whether it's for the beginning of a meal, part of a cocktail party or a light meal, hors d'oeuvres and appetizers don't have to be full of fat and calories Room can be made for these tasty tantalizing tidbits to add variety and pizzazz to a healthy diet. Old favourites can be modified to cut the fat without compromising the flavours you've enjoyed. Try some of our tasty recipes, or adjust your own recipes to fit the healthy eating guidelines.

Try some of the following ideas:

• For creamy dips, think low fat dairy products. Skim milk yogurt, low or nonfat sour cream, 1% cottage cheese, 2% ricotta cheese or 1.5% buttermilk can be used.

• Most salsas, antipasto, chutneys and bean dips are usually fine as is. You probably won't notice much difference if you reduced the amount of oil, or left it out altogether.

• Go easy on the meat (or chicken or fish) and heavier on the vegetables when planning your appetizers. If you plan to have a "meaty" appetizer you might serve a lighter main course or a meatless meal.

• Fried breaded seafood, sausage rolls and chicken wings can send your "fat budget" through the roof. Better choices are chicken or seafood kabobs and grilled or fresh vegetables marinated in light dressing. Try some of the marinades on pages 112-120.

• Instead of using rich crackers or tart shells, try toast cups or some of the new wonderful breads available such as multigrain, foccacia, sundried tomato or herb.

• Replace pate, salami and other high fat processed meats with ham, smoked turkey breast or smoked salmon. Serve with Dijon or honey mustard, or light cream cheese seasoned with your favorite herbs.

• Eye appeal is almost as important as flavour to tempt your taste buds. Instead of usual serving dishes, use a "vegetable cup" to serve dips and spreads. Select a vegetable such as sweet pepper, red cabbage or round squash, scoop out the insides and fill with dip. For garnishes use edible flowers, fresh whole herbs, and colourful fruit for a more tempting presentation.

HERBED CLAM DIP
Irene Stiles

This tasty dip is much lower in fat and calories than dips made with cream cheese, sour cream or mayonnaise. Serve with fresh vegetables.

1 cup	1% cottage cheese	250 mL
1 can	clams (5 oz/142 g)	1 can
1/4 cup	fresh parsley, chopped	50 mL
3 Tbsp	plain skim yogurt	45 mL
1 Tbsp	onion, minced	15 mL
2 tsp	fresh dill, chopped (or 1/2 tsp/2 mL dried dill)	10 mL
1	garlic clove, minced	1
dash	hot pepper sauce	dash
	pepper to taste	

In a blender or food processor, process cottage cheese until smooth. Drain clams, reserving 1 Tbsp/15 mL of the liquid. In a medium size bowl, combine all ingredients including reserved juice and mix well. Refrigerate for at least 1 hour or up to a day.

Makes about 2 cups/500 mL.

Nutritional analysis per 1 Tbsp/15 mL:
9 calories   1 g protein   0 g fat   1 g carbohydrate   3 mg cholesterol

---

Clams, unlike shrimp, have a cholesterol content similar to "finned fish". Steamed clams dipped in a vegetable broth rather than butter make great appetizers or even a main course.

EGGPLANT DIP WITH TAHINI

Waseem Ghurani

Eggplant is a relative newcomer to the western vegetable scene, but recently this versatile vegetable has become quite common in the market place and restaurants. Grilling the eggplant adds a delightful smoky taste to this otherwise mild-flavoured vegetable. Serve hot or cold with melba rounds or pita crisps.

1	large eggplant	1
3 Tbsp	tahini	45 mL
1/2	lemon	1/2
3	garlic cloves, finely chopped	3

Prick the eggplant with a fork. Place the whole eggplant on a baking sheet and cook at 400°F for 40 – 45 minutes, or grill over high heat for 1 hour until black and blistered. Let cool, and peel the skin off. Puree in a food processor or, mash the flesh with a fork until smooth. Stir in the tahini, juice of 1/2 lemon and garlic cloves. Mix well.

Makes 2 cup/500 mL.

Nutritional analysis per 2 Tbsp/30 mL:
20 calories   1 g protein   1 g fat   2 g carbohydrate   0 mg cholesterol

Tahini is sesame paste and can be found in the specialty section of most grocery stores. Use in small amounts because sesame seeds are high in fat. Even a "dab" will give you the flavour you want. If you don't have tahini a teaspoon of sesame oil can be used as a substitute.

SPICY EGGPLANT DIP
Maria Ragone

Serve this in a colourful bowl or a hollowed out pepper and garnish with chopped parsley.

2 Tbsp	olive oil	30 mL
1	onion, chopped	1
1	eggplant, peeled and cubed	1
1 tsp	cumin	5 mL
1	lemon	1
	salt to taste	
	cayenne to taste	

In a saucepan, heat oil and sauté onions, eggplant and spices for 2 minutes. Simmer for an additional 20 minutes, until eggplant is soft. Add the juice of one lemon. Mash slightly with the back of a fork. Spice to taste.

Makes 2 1/2 cup/625 mL.

Nutritional analysis per 2 Tbsp/30 mL:
19 calories   0 g protein   1 g fat   2 g carbohydrate   0 mg cholesterol

SPINACH DIP

This dip is much lower in fat than the traditional spinach dip which is made with sour cream and mayonnaise. Serve this in a hollowed out sourdough "bread bowl" with vegetable sticks and bread cubes.

2 cups	fat free sour cream	500 mL
3/4 cup	Miracle Whip™ light	200 mL
1 pkg	frozen spinach (10 oz/300 g) thawed and drained	1 pkg
1/4 cup	water chestnuts, chopped	50 mL
2 Tbsp	Knorr™ vegetable soup mix, dry	30 mL
4	green onions, chopped	4

Blend sour cream, Miracle Whip™, soup mix and onions together in food processor. Add spinach and water chestnuts and mix well.

Makes 3 cups/750 mL.

Nutritional analysis per 2 Tbsp/30 mL:
30 calories   1 g protein   2 g fat   4 carbohydrate   0 mg cholesterol

YOGURT AND CUCUMBER DIP

Waseem Ghurani

A delicious refreshing appetizer that is so easy to make. It is also a great accompaniment for fish instead of rich tartar sauce.

1	long english cucumber	1
2 cups	plain low fat yogurt	500 mL
1 Tbsp	fresh peppermint leaves, chopped	15 mL
3	garlic cloves, minced	3
	salt to taste	

Chop cucumber finely with a knife or process coarsely in the food processor. Mix all ingredients together in a medium size bowl. Refrigerate for 2 hours before serving.

Makes 3 cups/750 mL.

Nutritional analysis per 1/3 cup/75mL:
38 calories   3 g protein   0 g fat   6 g carbohydrate   1 mg cholesterol

Not all yogurts are low in milk fat (MF). Make sure you read the labels to help you make the best choice. Aim for a yogurt 2% MF or less. When making "dips" there is usually little difference in flavour whether you use 2% or even FAT FREE yogurt.

YOGURT CHEESE

Yogurt cheese is just drained yogurt. The longer you let it sit the thicker it will get.

To make yogurt cheese, use nonfat plain yogurt that does not contain starch, gums or gelatin. Line a sieve with a double thickness of cheesecloth and place over a large bowl. Add the yogurt to the cheesecloth lined sieve, cover with a plastic wrap and refrigerate overnight. Discard the liquid and store the cheese in a covered container. It will keep for up to 1 week. Three cups/750 mL of yogurt will make about 1 cup/250 mL of yogurt cheese.
This can be used as a spread as is, or try one of the following variations.

Nutritional analysis for 1 cup/250 mL of yogurt cheese:
372 calories   37 g protein   1 g fat   53 g carbohydrate   14 mg cholesterol

HONEYED YOGURT CHEESE

Use this as a topping for pancakes, waffles or french toast (low fat of course!).

1 cup	**yogurt cheese**	**250 mL**
2 Tbsp	**honey**	**30 mL**
1/4 cup	**concentrated frozen orange juice**	**50 mL**
	grated rind of 1 orange	

Combine all ingredients together and mix until well blended.

Makes 1 cup/250 mL.

HERBED YOGURT CHEESE

Serve this with crusty fresh bread.

2 cups	**yogurt cheese**	**500 mL**
2	**green onions, minced**	**2**
2 Tbsp	**fresh parsley, chopped**	**30 mL**
1	**garlic clove, minced**	**1**
	salt and pepper to taste	

In a medium size bowl blend together all ingredients and mix well. The cheese may be prepared ahead and stored covered in the refrigerator for up to 2 days.

Makes 2 cups/500 mL.

MEXICALI DIP
Shauna Ratner

Make sure you read the labels when you're buying "Refried Beans" – traditional styles are made with lard. Many vegetarian styles made with vegetable oil, and fat free varieties are now available. Serve with baked low fat tortilla chips available at your local grocery store or cut up vegetables.

1 can	vegetarian refried beans (14 oz/398 mL)	1 can
1/3 cup	plain skim milk yogurt	75 mL
2	green onions, chopped	2
1 tsp	cumin	5 mL
1/2 tsp	cayenne pepper	2 mL
2 Tbsp	fresh cilantro, chopped	30 mL
1	jalapeno pepper, seeded and finely diced	1

In a medium size bowl mash up the refried beans with a fork. Add yogurt, green onions, jalapeno pepper and spices. Blend well and chill. Sprinkle with cilantro before serving.

Makes 2 cups/500 mL.

Nutritional analysis per 2 Tbsp/30 mL:
30 calories   2 g protein   0 g fat   5 g carbohydrate   2 mg cholesterol

For party fare try this: In a quiche pan layer refried beans (or Mexicali Dip), fat free sour cream, salsa, a sprinkling of part skim cheese and top with chopped fresh tomatoes and green onions. Serve with baked low fat tortilla chips.

TURKEY SPREAD

A great way to use turkey leftovers! This spread can be used on canapes as appetizers, or in sandwiches for lunch, or as a main course salad for a light meal.

1 cup	cooked turkey, diced	250 mL
1	celery stalk	1
1 Tbsp	green onions, finely chopped	15 mL
1/4 cup	dried cranberries	50 mL
3 Tbsp	low fat mayonnaise	45 mL
1/4 tsp	sage	1 mL

salt and pepper to taste

Combine all ingredients. Mix well. Serve as a spread on crackers, mini sized pita bread or on cocktail bread slices. Garnish with parsley sprigs or sweet pickles.

Makes 1 1/2 cups (375 mL).

Nutritional analysis per 1/4 cup:
75 calories   5 g protein   3 g fat   7 g carbohydrate   13 mg cholesterol

Remember 1 tablespoon of regular mayonnaise is 11 grams of fat! If regular mayonnaise is used in making chicken salad, tuna salad, or even potato salad, the fat content can sky rocket.

CRISPS

These are healthy alternatives to "store bought" chips.

FLOUR TORTILLA CRISPS

Preheat oven to 325°F.
Use fresh tortillas which are available in the deli section of most grocery stores. Place tortillas in a single layer directly on to oven racks. Bake for 10 – 15 minutes turning once until slightly browned and crisp. Break into chip size pieces and serve with your favourite salsa.

Nutritional analysis per flour tortilla:
95 calories   3 g protein   2 g fat   17 g carbohydrate   0 mg cholesterol

PITA CRISPS

Preheat oven to 350°F.
Open the pita pockets into two shells. Cut each round into eight triangles. Place on a baking sheet and bake for 10 minutes until crisp. Serve with a tangy bean dip or hummus.

Nutritional analysis per 1 pita bread:
105 calories   4 g protein   1 g fat   21 g carbohydrate   0 mg cholesterol

BAGEL CRISPS

Preheat oven to 350°F.
Choose flavoured bagels such as onion or cinnamon raisin. Slice each bagel into 1/8 in/.5 cm rounds. Place on baking sheet and bake for 10 – 15 minutes until crisp. These are great as is!

Nutritional analysis per 1 bagel:
167 calories   6 g protein   1 g fat   33 g carbohydrate   15 mg cholesterol

BRUSCHETTA
Shauna Ratner

Traditional bruschetta is thickly sliced bread grilled over an open fire and rubbed with garlic, olive oil and salt. To dress it up add fresh tomatoes, fresh basil, a splash of balsamic vinegar, chopped sundried tomatoes, capers, roasted peppers or any combination of these. This particular recipe bursts with flavour in summer using fresh vine-ripened tomatoes and fresh herbs from the garden.

4	**tomatoes, finely diced**	4
1/4 cup	**fresh basil leaves, chopped**	50 mL
1/4 cup	**fresh parsley, chopped**	50 mL
3	**garlic cloves**	3
2	**green onions, chopped (optional)**	2
1 Tbsp	**olive oil**	15 mL
	wine vinegar or lemon juice to taste	
	salt to taste	
1/2	**baguette, cut into 16 slices**	1/2

In a medium size bowl combine diced tomatoes, 1 garlic clove minced, green onions, basil and parsley. Add olive oil, wine vinegar or lemon juice and salt and pepper to taste. Toss well and set aside for at least 15 minutes to let flavours mix together.

Just before serving, toast the bread and rub one side with the cut side of a garlic clove. Spoon tomato mixture over the bread and serve immediately.

Makes 16 slices.

Nutritional analysis per 1 slice:
50 calories   1 g protein   1 g fat   8 g carbohydrate   0 mg cholesterol

If you rub a cut garlic clove over hot toast the clove will "melt" and give the bread a wonderful flavour. This is the perfect way to make fat free garlic toast or croutons.

DOLMATHES

Ruth Grierson

In Greek "Dolmas" indicates a food that is stuffed. This recipe for dolmathes uses the exotic, but edible grape leaves. These grape leaves are found in a jar at your local supermarket. Serve this on a colourful Mediterranean style plate with yogurt and cucumber dip and garnish with lemon wedges.

1 jar	**vine leaves (grape leaves)**	**1 jar**
1	**tomato, chopped**	**1**
3/4 cup	**long grain rice, uncooked**	**200 mL**
1/4 cup	**pine nuts**	**50 mL**
1	**garlic clove**	**1**
	rind of 1 lemon, grated	
1 bunch	**green onions, chopped**	**1 bunch**
1 1/2 Tbsp	**fresh dill, chopped**	**22 mL**
1/4 cup	**seedless currants, chopped**	**50 mL**
	(soak in 1/2 cup/125 mL white wine)	
1 Tbsp	**parsley, chopped**	**15 mL**
2 cups	**chicken stock**	**500 mL**
1 Tbsp	**olive oil**	**15 mL**
	salt and pepper to taste	

Remove leaves from the jar and rinse in a warm water bath at least 3 times to remove brine. Cut off stems from leaves. Drain on paper towels.

In a skillet, sauté onions, garlic, and parsley in oil. Add rice, dill, pine nuts, currants, wine, lemon rind, salt, pepper and tomato. Bring to a boil, reduce heat and simmer until the liquid evaporates. Cool.

Place grape leaf shiny side down. Put a teaspoon of the rice mixture in bottom centre, cover filling by folding end first, then sides and roll in a 2 in/5 cm cylinder.

Arrange stuffed grape leaves in circular layers in a heavy pot. Pour stock and lemon juice over dolmathes and weigh down with a heavy plate. Bring to a boil and immediately lower heat. Simmer over low heat for 1 1/2 hours. Add more stock if necessary. Chill before serving. These can be made up to 2 days in advance.

Makes 50 stuffed grape leaves.

Nutritional analysis per roll:
23 calories   0 g protein   1 g fat   4 g carbohydrate   0 mg cholesterol

NUTS N' BITES

There is no end to what you can add to this power packed snack full of fiber and low in fat! Slice up dried apricots, dried cranberries or cherries, banana chips and any combination of your favourite bite sized cereals and mix it in. Take a bag of it with you on your next hike or munch on it on the way to work if you are in a rush for breakfast.

6 cups	mixed cereals	1.5 L
(e.g. Corn bran™, Shreddies™, Cheerios™ etc.)		
1 cup	pretzels	250 mL
1 cup	small crackers (e.g. goldfish)	250 mL
1 cup	raisins	250 mL
1/4 cup	peanuts	50 mL

Mix all ingredients together in a large mixing bowl.

Makes 9 1/4 cups/2.3 L.

Nutritional analysis per 1 cup/250 mL:
194 calories   5 g protein   4 g fat   39 g carbohydrate   0 mg cholesterol

SOUPS

Nothing is more welcoming than the aroma of homemade soup bubbling on the stove on a cool autumn evening. The variations for soups are endless - there is really no limit to what you can add to the soup pot. Make a light soup for a first course, or serve a heartier soup with a slice of crusty bread and a tossed salad for a meal in itself.

Try some of the following ideas:

• If the recipe calls for oil or margarine for sautéing vegetables, cut it down, or better yet, leave it out. Use a bit of chicken or beef broth, or some of the juice from canned tomatoes instead. You won't miss the fat at all.

• Use 1%, skim or canned evaporated skim milk instead of whole milk to make cream soups.

• Replace the roux (butter and flour mixture) with a slurry (cornstarch or flour dissolved in a liquid) to thicken your soup.

• For a thick hearty soup, add potatoes, rice, pasta, beans or pureed vegetables.

• To add more flavour and nutrition to canned or packaged soups, add left-over chicken or lean meat, pasta, beans, or any vegetables.

• If you're making your own stock it's best to make it the night before and set it in the refrigerator overnight. Just skim off that layer of hardened fat the next day.

• Try making fruit soups or serving a chilled soup when the weather is hot.

• For a change, roast vegetables before adding them to the soup pot to give a more robust flavour with little fat.

ONE CUP NAVY BEAN SOUP
Velma Stebner

A deliciously light yet filling soup. For a tasty shortcut use one large can of beans instead of cooking the dried beans. Simply combine all ingredients together and simmer until vegetables are tender.

1 cup	**dried navy beans, soaked overnight**	**250 mL**
1 cup	**onion, chopped**	**250 mL**
1 cup	**carrots, chopped**	**250 mL**
1 cup	**celery, chopped**	**250 mL**
1 cup	**turnip, chopped**	**250 mL**
1 cup	**potatoes, diced**	**250 mL**
1	**bay leaf**	**1**
1 cup	**lean ham, diced**	**250 mL**
1 cup	**lettuce, shredded**	**250 mL**

salt and pepper to taste

In a large saucepan, combine 10 cups/2.5 L of water and beans. Bring to a boil. Reduce heat and simmer, partially covered for 1 1/2 hours or until beans are tender.

Add onions, carrots, celery, turnips, potatoes, and bay leaf. Simmer for 20 minutes. Add ham and lettuce. Simmer 5 minutes. Season with salt and pepper.

Serves 12.

Nutritional analysis per serving:
84 Calories   6 g protein   1 g fat   15 g carbohydrate   8 mg cholesterol

If you want to have soup for a main course, add extra beans or lean meat and top with grated low fat cheese. Serve with a tossed green salad and fresh rolls.

SPLIT PEA SOUP
Linda Vicic

This vegetarian split pea soup is thick and wholesome. You won't even miss the meat.

5 cups	**defatted chicken stock or vegetarian broth**	**1.25 L**
1 cup	**split peas, dry**	**250 mL**
1	**carrot, chopped**	**1**
1	**celery stalk, chopped**	**1**
1	**small onion, chopped**	**1**
1	**leek, white part only, chopped**	**1**
1 tsp	**thyme**	**5 mL**
1	**garlic clove, chopped**	**1**

Bouquet Garni (2 bay leaves, 1/2 tsp/2 mL thyme, parsley sprigs, and celery leaves) (see below for directions to make)

Combine chicken or vegetable stock, split peas, bouquet garni and garlic in a medium size stock pot and simmer for 20 minutes. Add carrots, celery, onion, leek and thyme and cook for an additional 40 minutes. Remove bouquet garni. Puree the soup in a blender until smooth. Heat thoroughly before serving.

Serves 6.

Nutritional analysis per serving:
104 calories   5 g protein   0 g fat   21 g carbohydrate   0 mg cholesterol   7 g fiber

Bouquet Garni is a mixture of French herbs tied together in a cheesecloth and boiled with the stock to add a wonderful variety of flavours. The bundle should always contain a bay leaf, thyme, and parsley. Sometimes other herbs like savory and tarragon can be used. Be sure to remove the packet before serving.

CREAMY CARROT SOUP
Ruth Saunders

Cream soups are usually higher in fat than desired, but when made with skim milk, the soup can be just as tasty yet low in fat. The spices in this carrot soup are especially interesting.

2	garlic cloves, minced	2
2	medium onions, chopped	2
1	celery stalk, chopped	1
3 cups	carrots, sliced	750 mL
1	small potato, peeled and cut up	1
4 cups	boiling water	1 L
4 Tbsp	instant chicken soup mix	60 mL
2 tsp	salt	10 mL
1/4 tsp	pepper	1 mL
1/2 tsp	thyme	2 mL
1/4 tsp	dried dill	1 mL
1 1/2 cups	skim milk	375 mL
1/4 cup	low fat mayonnaise	50 mL

Put all ingredients except milk and mayonnaise together in a microwave proof dish. Cook in microwave oven uncovered on high power for 25 minutes. Add milk and mayonnaise and puree if desired. Garnish with parsley and serve hot.

Serves 10.

Nutritional analysis per serving:
73 Calories   3 g protein   2 g fat   12 g carbohydrate   3 mg cholesterol

Carrots are packed with beta-carotene, a form of vitamin A, and an antioxidant. Antioxidants are thought to help protect against heart disease.

HARVEST SOUP
Maria Ragone

An abundance of beans, pasta and vegetables makes this nutrient packed soup ideal for lunch. Serve it with crusty fresh bread and low fat cheese.

1 cup	onions, chopped	250 mL
3 Tbsp	garlic, minced	45 mL
1 cup	carrots, minced	250 mL
1/4 cup	fresh parsley, minced	50 mL
1 tsp	oregano	5 mL
1 tsp	basil	5 mL
1/2 tsp	thyme	2 mL
1/4 cup	red cooking wine	50 mL
1/2 cup	celery, chopped	125 mL
1 cup	cabbage, sliced	250 mL
1 cup	vegetable stock or water	250 mL
1 cup	great northern beans, cooked	250 mL
1 1/2 cup	tomato, chopped	375 mL
1/4 tsp	cloves	1 mL
1/4 cup	tomato paste	50 mL
1 cup	apple juice	250 mL
2 cups	vegetable juice cocktail	500 mL
1 cup	zucchini, sliced	250 mL
1/4 cup	macaroni, dry	50 mL

Sauté onions, garlic, carrots and spices in red wine until onions are soft. Add celery, cabbage and vegetable stock or water and simmer 5 minutes. Stir occasionally. Add beans, tomatoes, cloves, tomato paste, apple juice and vegetable juice cocktail and bring to a boil. Reduce heat and simmer for 15 minutes. Add zucchini and simmer 2 minutes. Add macaroni and cook for about 8 minutes or until pasta is al dente.

Serves 6.

Nutritional analysis per serving:
157 Calories   6 g protein   1 g fat   32 g carbohydrate   0 mg cholesterol   5 g fiber

When pasta is cooked just right, it is cooked "al dente" which literally translates as "to the tooth." The pasta should be tender, but still have a bite to it.

CLAM CHOWDER
Frances Johnson

New England clam chowder is usually creamy and too rich. Tomato based Manhattan style chowders are just as tasty without all that fat.

2 oz	lean ham, chopped	60g
2	celery stalks, chopped	2
1	onion, chopped	1
1 Tbsp	flour	15 mL
2 cups	water	500 mL
3	medium potatoes, peeled and diced	3
1 can	stewed tomatoes (14 oz/396 mL)	1 can
1 can	whole baby clams (5 oz/142 g), including liquid	1 can
1	bay leaf	1
1/2 tsp	salt	2 mL
1/4 tsp	sugar	1 mL
1/4 tsp	thyme	1 mL

In a large pot, combine ham, celery and onion. Cook until vegetables are softened. Sprinkle flour into pan and stir until blended. Stir in water and bring to boil.

Add potatoes, tomatoes, liquid from clams and seasonings. Simmer about 20 minutes or until potatoes are tender. Add clams and simmer 3 more minutes. Remove bay leaf before serving.

Serves 6.

Nutritional analysis per serving:
124 Calories   9 g protein   1 g fat   22 g carbohydrate   35 mg cholesterol

HAMBURGER SOUP

Brian Goring

This hearty soup is so easy to prepare. Make it ahead of time and freeze – it's a perfect supper for a chilly fall day.

1 1/2 lb	extra lean ground beef	680g
1	onion, chopped	1
1 can	tomatoes (28 oz/796 mL)	1 can
2 cups	water	500 mL
3 cans	consommé soup (10 oz/284 mL)	3 cans
1 can	tomato soup (10 oz /284 mL)	1 can
1	bay leaf	1
3	celery stalks, chopped	3
1 tsp	parsley	5 mL
8 Tbsp	pearl barley, uncooked	120 mL

In a large nonstick pan, brown ground beef until well cooked. Drain off the liquid and set the meat aside.

Sauté the onion in a medium size soup pot until softened. Add the cooked ground beef and the remaining ingredients . Stir well and simmer covered for 2 hours.

Serves 10.

Nutrient analysis per serving:
268 Calories   19 g protein   13 g fat   21 g carbohydrate   46 mg cholesterol

Regular ground beef can have as much fat as sausages! Be sure to choose the leanest type possible. Ground chicken and turkey are good alternatives, but make sure that not too much skin or other fatty parts are used. Drain off all fat after browning.

MINESTRONE STYLE SOUP
John Devereux

This easy to prepare soup is great as a starter for a meatless meal. Team it up with a veggie burger and vegetable sticks.

5-6 cups	water	1.25-1.5 L
5-6	carrots, sliced	5-6
2	celery stalks, diced	2
1	onion, chopped	1
1 can	tomatoes (28 oz/796 mL), chopped	1 can
1 can	kidney beans (14 oz/398 mL), drained	1 can
2 cups	fusilli pasta, dry	500 mL
1 cup	frozen peas	250 mL
	salt and pepper to taste	
	hot pepper sauce, optional	

In a large saucepan, bring water to a boil. Add carrots, celery, onion, tomatoes, and kidney beans. Mix well. Simmer covered for 25 minutes. Cook fusilli according to package directions. Stir in fusilli and peas to soup mixture and heat through. Season to taste with salt, pepper, and hot pepper sauce. Add more water and seasonings as desired.

Serves 12.

Nutritional analysis per serving:
125 Calories   6 g protein   1 g fat   25 g carbohydrate   0 mg cholesterol   5 g fiber

There are over 200 different types of pastas with various shapes, sizes and flavours. Mix and match pastas such as fusilli, rotini, shells, linguine, spinach or whole wheat. Watch out for filled pastas such as tortillini or ravioli, as they are often filled with high fat ingredients.

LENTIL AND BROWN RICE SOUP
Maria Ragone

Having this nutritious lentil soup for a main course is a great way of keeping your fat intake down and your fiber intake up.

5 cups	chicken broth	1.25 L
3 cups	water	750 mL
1 1/2 cups	lentils, uncooked (rinsed and picked over)	375 mL
1 cup	brown rice, uncooked	250 mL
1 can	diced tomatoes (35 oz/1 L), undrained	1 can
3	carrots, chopped	3
1	onion, chopped	1
1	celery stalk, chopped	1
3	garlic cloves, minced	3
1/2 tsp	basil	2 mL
1/2 tsp	oregano	2 mL
1/4 tsp	thyme	1 mL
1	bay leaf	1
1/2 cup	fresh parsley, minced	125 mL
	salt and pepper to taste	

In a large pot, combine chicken broth, water, lentils, rice, tomatoes, carrots, onion, celery, garlic, basil, oregano, thyme and bay leaf. Cover and bring to a boil. Simmer for 45 – 55 minutes until lentils and rice are tender. Stir in parsley, salt and pepper. Discard bay leaf. Soup will be thick and will thicken further as it stands. If desired, thin with additional hot chicken broth or water.

Serves 8.

Nutritional analysis per serving:
242 Calories   13 g protein   1 g fat   46 g carbohydrate   0 mg cholesterol   8 g fiber

Lentils do not require soaking as other dried legumes do, but rinse them before using. One cup of lentils will expand to about 2 to 2 1/2 cups after cooking.

HOT AND SOUR SOUP

Eunice Melton

The idea of "hot and sour" may seem unusual for a soup, but the combination is delicious in this hearty soup. Serve it with a plate of steamed vegetables and rice for a simple meal.

1	**medium chicken breast half**	1
2 cups	**hot water**	**500 mL**
1	**carrot, cut into sticks**	1
1	**celery stalk, cut into sticks**	1
1 tsp or less	**salt, (optional)**	**5 mL or less**
1/2 cup	**fresh mushrooms, sliced**	**125 mL**
1 Tbsp	**cornstarch**	**15 mL**
1/2 tsp	**pepper**	**2 mL**
1 Tbsp	**white wine vinegar**	**15 mL**
2 tsp	**soy sauce**	**10 mL**
1/2 tsp	**sesame oil**	**2 mL**
2	**egg whites, slightly beaten**	**2**
1	**green onion, cut into thin diagonal pieces**	1

In 1 1/2 qt/1.5 L casserole dish, combine chicken, water, carrot, celery, and salt. Cover and microwave on high for 8 to 10 minutes, or until chicken is no longer pink, turning meat over and stirring broth after half the time. Remove chicken and vegetables. Reserve liquid. Cool chicken and discard vegetables (or use them as a side dish).

Skin and bone chicken. Cut into matchstick pieces. Add chicken and mushrooms to broth. Microwave at high for 4 to 6 minutes, or until boiling. Mix cornstarch, pepper, vinegar, soy sauce and sesame oil. Stir into broth. Microwave at high for 1 to 2 minutes or until slightly thickened, stirring after half the time. Stir soup. Pour slightly beaten egg white in thin stream into soup, stirring in a circular motion. Sprinkle with green onion pieces.

Serves 2.

Nutritional analysis per serving:
184 Calories   23 g protein   4 g fat   13 g carbohydrate   47 mg cholesterol

Using just a little of these low fat sauces can "spice up" steamed vegetables: light soy sauce, hoisin sauce, sweet and sour sauce, or low calorie Italian dressing.

VEGETABLES AND SALADS

According to Canada's Guide to Healthy Eating you need to eat 5 – 10 servings of fruits and vegetables each day. That might seem like a lot...but think about this:

• Vegetables are loaded with vitamins and minerals including the antioxidants you hear so much about these days. Vitamins A, C and E and minerals such as iron and calcium are just a few of these important nutrients. Trace vitamins and minerals and probably even those we haven't yet discovered are housed inside those vegetables that seem so common.

• Vegetables are one of our main sources of fiber. Eating plenty of fiber promotes regularity, reduces your risk for developing some cancers and helps control blood cholesterol levels.

• Most vegetables only have a trace of fat, except avocado and olives, yet they fill us up without giving us too many calories.

• They provide variety in colour, flavour and texture in our diet. Eat them as an accompaniment to a meal, as a snack or even make a main meal from them.

• Cook vegetables just about any way – boil, steam, bake, roast, stir fry, grill or barbecue. You can even eat them raw!

• Eat them whole or cut them up. Serve them julienned, diced, chopped, mashed or skewer them on a kabob.

• Eat vegetables plain or serve them with a low fat dip, or sprinkle with lemon juice, soy sauce or a splash of balsamic vinegar for a taste treat.

• Salads are usually healthy, but be careful with the dressing. Regular salad dressings can add lots of extra calories and fat! Cut the oil by one half and use yogurt, chicken broth, buttermilk or flavoured vinegar. Add fresh herbs, Dijon mustard or mustard powder to boost the flavour.

So, think **vegetables** when it comes to adding zest and nutrition to your diet. Then put your culinary talents to work...and enjoy!!!

ROASTED ASPARAGUS

Frances Johnson

Roasting at a high temperature enhances the natural flavour of asparagus.

1 lb	fresh asparagus	454 g
1 tsp	olive oil	5 mL
	salt to taste	

Preheat oven to 450°F. Snap tough ends off and lay asparagus on baking sheet in single layer. Drizzle oil over asparagus. Roll asparagus around until oil is spread out. Sprinkle with salt to taste. Bake for 8 – 10 minutes until asparagus are "roasted".

Serves 4.

Nutritional analysis per serving:
36 calories   3 g protein   2 g fat   2 g carbohydrate   0 mg cholesterol

Roasted new potatoes are delicious. Cut potatoes in halves or quarters, mix with a touch of olive oil and a sprinkling of salt. Place on a baking sheet in a single layer. Roast at 375°F for about 45 minutes or until done. Mixing a little dried rosemary and a minced garlic clove along with the olive oil adds a more aromatic flavour.

FRESH BEANS WITH SESAME SAUCE
Emiko Pang

This is a good salad to make in the summer time when the beans are fresh and plentiful. For extra colour mix together green and yellow beans.

1 lb	fresh beans	454 g
3 Tbsp	sesame seeds	45 mL
2 1/2 Tbsp	soy sauce	40 mL
1 tsp	brown sugar, packed	5 mL

In a large pot of boiling water, cook beans for 5 minutes. Drain and rinse under cold water. Cut beans into bite sized pieces. In a large bowl toss together beans and 1/2 tsp/2 mL soy sauce. Set aside.

Heat sesame seeds in a nonstick pan until a few seeds start jumping. Remove from heat. Place sesame seeds on a plate and mash or grind fine with a mortar and pestle. Add remaining soy sauce and sugar and mix well. Pour over bean mixture just before serving.

Serves 4.

Nutritional analysis per serving:
88 calories   4 g protein   4 g fat   12 g carbohydrate   0 mg cholesterol

Beans come in many different shapes, sizes and colours, but all are good sources of vitamin C, vitamin A, potassium and fiber. So be adventurous and try some of the endless varieties available such as Scarlett Runners, Romano, Chinese long and wax beans.

GREEN BEANS ITALIANO
Debbie DeAngelis

You can't beat steamed green beans fresh from the garden, especially when seasoned with a Mediterranean touch.

1 lb	green beans	454 g
1 Tbsp	olive oil	15 mL
1 tsp	dried oregano	5 mL
1 tsp	garlic powder	5 mL
1/4 tsp	salt	1 mL
	dash red wine vinegar	

Steam green beans until tender. Let cool. Toss with remaining ingredients.

Serves 4.

Nutritional analysis per serving:
70 calories   2 g protein   4 g fat   9 g carbohydrate   0 mg cholesterol

Frozen green beans are a better choice than canned for nutrition, flavour and texture. But in the summer, take advantage of the fresh green beans available in abundance.

WHITE BEAN SALAD
Ruth Grierson

Bean salads improve with time as flavours mellow. Leftovers are great as part of a brown bag lunch.

1 1/4 cups	small white beans, dry	300 mL
1	tomato, chopped	1
1/2	red onion, chopped	1/2
1/4 cup	pitted black olives, chopped	50 mL
2 Tbsp	olive oil	30 mL
3 Tbsp	white wine vinegar	45 mL
1	garlic clove, chopped	1
	salt and pepper to taste	
1/4 cup	fresh basil, chopped	50 mL

Soak beans in water overnight. In large saucepan, add beans and enough water to cover by 2 in/5 cm. Bring to a boil and simmer until beans are tender, about 45 minutes to 1 hour. Drain beans and set aside to cool.

In large bowl, combine beans with remaining ingredients except basil. Mix to coat well. Cover and refrigerate. Just before serving add fresh basil.

Serves 6.

Nutritional analysis per serving:
198 calories   9 g protein   7 g fat   26 g carbohydrate   0 mg cholesterol   6 g fiber

Beans, once thought of as "poor man's meat" have become the winning choice of health conscious individuals. Beans are popping up everywhere...in veggie burgers, tofu products and soy cheese!

GLADYS' BEAN SALAD
Isobel Webster

Water chestnuts add an interesting crunch to this classic bean salad. Almost any combination of your favourite beans can be used. The addition of pasta makes this especially delightful.

1 can	**green beans, drained** **(14 oz/398 mL)**	1 can
1 can	**garbanzo beans or lima beans,** **drained(14 oz/398 mL)**	1 can
1 can	**kidney beans, drained** **(14 oz/398 mL)**	1 can
1 can	**water chestnuts,** **drained and sliced (10 oz/284 mL)**	1 can
1	**small red onion, sliced thinly**	1
1 cup	**cooked pasta, rotini** **or penne (optional)**	250 mL
1/3 cup	**sugar**	75 mL
1/3 cup	**olive oil**	75 mL
1/3 cup	**vinegar**	75 mL
1/2 tsp	**salt**	2 mL
1/4 tsp	**dry mustard**	1 mL
1/4 tsp	**tarragon**	1 mL
1/4 tsp	**basil**	1 mL

Mix beans, water chestnuts, onions and pasta (if using). Set aside. Mix together remaining ingredients and pour over bean mixture. Let sit in the refrigerator for a few hours before serving.

Serves 12.

Nutritional analysis per serving:
163 calories   4 g protein   7 g fat   21 g carbohydrate   0 mg cholesterol   5 g fiber

If you don't have time to soak dry beans, canned beans are a convenient substitute.

ALL-SPICE CABBAGE
Maria Ragone

This easy to make tangy vegetable dish is a good accompaniment for meat or poultry. Red cabbage can be substituted for added colour. This also tastes great cold.

1/2 head	cabbage, shredded	1/2 head
1/2	onion, sliced	1/2
1 cup	water	250 mL
2 Tbsp	vinegar	30 mL
2 Tbsp	brown or white sugar	30 mL
1/2 tsp	thyme	2 mL
1/4 tsp	allspice	1 mL

Put cabbage and onion in frying pan with water. Cover and cook 15 to 20 minutes, stirring occasionally. Drain all the water. Add vinegar, sugar, thyme and allspice. Mix well.

Serves 6.

Nutritional analysis per serving:
41 calories   1 g protein   0 g fat   10 g carbohydrate   0 mg cholesterol

The cabbage family includes versatile vegetables such as broccoli, brussel sprouts and cauliflower. Gai lan, bok choi, sui choi and choi sum are but a few of the more recent arrivals to neighbourhood markets. Be sure to make these a regular part of your diet.

RED CABBAGE WITH APPLES

Wernel Kissel

The apples give the cabbage a sweet tangy taste. An added bonus is that it's completely fat free!

1	**head red cabbage, shredded**	1
2	**large apples, peeled and thinly sliced**	2
1/4 cup	**unsweetened apple juice**	50 mL
1/4 cup	**fresh lemon juice**	50 mL
1	**onion, sliced**	1
2 Tbsp	**raisins**	30 mL
2 Tbsp	**brown sugar**	30 mL

salt and pepper to taste

Toss all ingredients together in a nonstick saucepan. Cover and simmer 30 – 35 minutes or until cabbage is soft.

Serves 12.

Nutritional analysis per serving:
61 calories   1 g protein   0 g fat   15 g carbohydrate   0 mg cholesterol

LIGHT COLESLAW
Maria Ragone

The apple and honey give this coleslaw a touch of sweetness. Make this in advance and keep it in the refrigerator for a quick salad.

2 Tbsp	apple juice	30 mL
1 Tbsp	vinegar	15 mL
2 tsp	Dijon mustard	10 mL
2 tsp	liquid honey	10 mL
2 Tbsp	oil	30 mL
1 Tbsp	fresh parsley, minced	15 mL
4 cups	green cabbage, thinly sliced	1 L
2	carrots, grated	2
2	celery stalks, julienned	2
1/2	small red apple, chopped	1/2
3	green onions, julienned	3
	salt and pepper to taste	

Whisk together apple juice, vinegar, Dijon mustard and honey. Gradually whisk in oil. Stir in parsley, salt and pepper. Set aside.

Mix remaining ingredients together. Add dressing to vegetable mixture. Toss well.

Serves 6.

Nutritional analysis per serving:
89 calories   1 g protein   5 g fat   12 g carbohydrate   0 mg cholesterol   3 g fiber

Cabbage has always been thought of as a winter vegetable since it stores so well. Make coleslaw in winter time when lettuce is expensive.

BAKED CARROTS AND RUTABAGA
Frances Johnson

Nutmeg and cinnamon are a sweet warm combo in this vegetable dish. Use whole young carrots for a more gourmet touch.

6	carrots, peeled	6
1	rutabaga	1
1 tsp	soft margarine	5 mL
2 Tbsp	maple syrup	30 mL
1/4 tsp	nutmeg	1 mL
1/4 tsp	cinnamon	1 mL

Preheat oven to 350°F. Cut carrots and turnip into sticks and place in casserole dish. Add remaining ingredients and cover dish. Bake for 45 minutes or until done, mixing once or twice while baking.

Serves 6.

Nutritional analysis per serving:
66 calories   1 g protein   1 g fat   15 g carbohydrate   0 mg cholesterol   3 g fiber

You can buy baby carrots pre-washed, pre-peeled and ready to eat. Nothing could be more convenient!

PEPPER AND MUSHROOM MEDLEY
Frances Johnson

Baking the peppers brings out their best flavour and texture. This colourful dish can be made any time of year, but is especially great in late summer when peppers are abundant.

2	**red peppers, sliced**	2
2	**yellow peppers, sliced**	2
2	**garlic cloves, minced**	2
2 Tbsp	**olive oil**	30 mL
3/4 lb	**mushrooms, sliced**	325 g
	juice of 1 lemon	
1 1/2 Tbsp	**sugar**	22 mL
1/4 tsp	**salt**	1 mL
2 Tbsp	**rice or wine vinegar**	30 mL
	black pepper to taste	

Mix together peppers, 1 Tbsp/15 mL olive oil and garlic. Spread out on baking sheet and bake in oven at 375°F for about 20 minutes or until tender. Let cool. In a bowl combine cooled peppers and sliced mushrooms. Set aside.

In a small bowl whisk together lemon juice, 1 Tbsp/15 mL olive oil, sugar, vinegar, salt and pepper. Add the dressing to mushroom and pepper mixture. Cover and marinate for 1 hour in refrigerator before serving.

Serves 10.

Nutritional analysis per serving:
51 calories   1 g protein   3 g fat   6 g carbohydrate   0 mg cholesterol

Sweet peppers are not only a good source of beta carotene but an excellent source of vitamin C. You can buy all different colours of peppers – orange, yellow, red and even purple! Mix all the colours together for that extra eye appeal!

No-Fry Home Fries

Regular french fries are loaded with fat – one potato made into fries can have as much as 1 tablespoon of oil! Pre-made frozen fries baked in the oven are not much better. These homemade chips are a wonderful low fat alternative.

4	potatoes	4
1/2 Tbsp	oil	7 mL
	salt to taste	

Wash potatoes well, but do not peel. Cut each potato into 8 wedges lengthwise. Put into large bowl and add oil. Mix until potatoes are lightly coated. Place potato wedges on a cookie sheet in a single layer. Sprinkle lightly with salt. Bake at 375°F for 35 – 45 minutes until cooked through and lightly browned. Serve with ketchup if desired.

Serves 4.

Nutritional analysis per serving:
111 calories   2 g protein   2 g fat   22 g carbohydrate   0 mg cholesterol

Potatoes are not fattening. Instead they provide energy, fiber, potassium and lots of B vitamins. It's the traditional toppings that send the calories and fat "over the top". Use non fat sour cream, yogurt, salsa or sautéed chopped vegetables as potato toppers rather that their higher fat counterparts.

SHERRIED SWEET POTATOES
Hugh Green

The unusual mixture of apples and sweet potatoes make a tasty duo as part of a harvest meal. The hint of sherry is a sensational touch.

3	yams or sweet potatoes	3
3	granny smith apples	3
1/4 cup	soft margarine	50 mL
1/4 cup	lemon juice	50 mL
1/4 cup	firmly packed brown sugar	50 mL
1/4 tsp	cinnamon	1 mL
1/3 cup	medium dry sherry	75 mL

In medium size pot, combine whole yams with enough cold water to cover them by 1 in/2.5 cm. Let boil for about 35 minutes, or until tender. Drain and let cool. Peel the yams and cut them lengthwise and then into 1/2 in/ 2 cm pieces. Set aside. Peel, core and cut the apples lengthwise into eighths and set aside.

Melt margarine in a heavy skillet over medium heat. Add the apples and sauté until tender, stirring frequently. Stir in the lemon juice, brown sugar, cinnamon and sherry. Bring the liquid to a boil and simmer the apple mixture for 3 minutes. Add the yams and cook the mixture, stirring gently until combined well and heated through. Transfer to a heated serving dish.

Serves 8.

Nutritional analysis per serving:
201 calories   1 g protein   6 g fat   35 g carbohydrate   0 mg cholesterol   3 g fiber

Sweet potatoes and yams are delicious wrapped in foil and baked in the oven. They are high in fiber and full of Beta carotene and vitamin C.

VEGETABLE STIR FRY

Barbara Kemp

There can be so many variations of stir frying with or without meat. This recipe uses a little vinegar for added flavour. You can adjust the amount of ginger and garlic to suit your taste.

1 Tbsp	soy sauce	15 mL
1 Tbsp	vinegar	15 mL
1 Tbsp	honey	15 mL
1 tsp	rice vinegar	5 mL
2 tsp	cornstarch	10 mL
1 Tbsp	fresh ginger, grated	15 mL
1	garlic clove, minced	1
1 Tbsp	oil	15 mL
4 cups	broccoli, carrots, cauliflower, green beans and mushrooms (any combination)	1 L
	tofu, cubed (if desired)	

Chop vegetables into bite sized pieces. Set aside.

Mix together soy sauce, vinegar, honey, rice vinegar, and cornstarch. Set aside.

Heat oil in large skillet or wok. Stir fry garlic and ginger for about 1 minute. Add vegetables. Stir fry until vegetables are tender-crisp, adding a little water if the pan is dry. Add sauce mixture and cook while stirring until sauce is thickened. Add tofu, if using, and stir fry gently until tofu is hot. Serve over rice.

Serves 4.

Nutritional analysis per serving (without tofu):
98 Calories   3 g protein   4 g fat   16 g carbohydrates   0 mg cholesterol   2 g fiber

If you would like to add meat to your stir fry, use thinly sliced lean beef or small bite sized pieces of skinless chicken breast. Sauté them first along with the garlic and ginger and stir fry until meat is cooked. Remove from pan and set aside. Add the vegetables into the same pan and sauté vegetables until done. Add the meat back to the pan and add the sauce mixture. Cook until sauce is thickened and meat is hot.

GRILLED VEGETABLES
Shauna Ratner

These are delicious in sandwiches, served as part of an antipasto plate for appetizers, or as a side dish for a barbecue dinner. You can also skewer bite size vegetables and grill them.

peppers, quartered
eggplant, sliced in thin rounds
zucchini, sliced diagonally
asparagus
mushrooms
olive oil
balsamic vinegar

Pre-heat gas barbecue or use coals once ready. Place vegetables on the grill. Put peppers skin side down. Brush lightly with olive oil and balsamic vinegar. When peppers are charred, turn over and cook other side slightly. Turn other vegetables over when slightly brown and cook until done.

Nutritional analysis will depend upon vegetables and amount of oil used – of course, use as little oil as possible!

Add leftover grilled vegetables to spaghetti sauce or to the soup pot for a delicious smoky flavour.

TOURLU
Lillian Dagenais

This is an Armenian version of the classic French ratatouille. It's a wonderful flavoured vegetable medley that can be served either hot or at room temperature. If you like spicy foods, add some red pepper flakes. Eat this on its own or serve it over pasta or rice. Vegetables in this dish look best when sliced into 1 – 1 1/2 inch pieces.

1 can	**Italian style tomatoes (1 lb/454 g), undrained**	1 can
2 Tbsp	**olive oil**	30 mL
1/2 cup	**ketchup**	125 mL
1 1/2 tsp each	**salt, sugar, basil**	7 mL each
1/4 tsp	**pepper**	1 mL
1/2 lb	**green beans, sliced**	225 g
2	**large potatoes, peeled and cubed**	2
3	**medium carrots, sliced diagonally**	3
2	**large onions, diced**	2
2	**celery stalks, sliced into chunks**	2
2	**large red or green peppers, diced**	2
1	**medium size eggplant, cubed**	1
3	**small zucchini, cubed**	3
	plain skim milk yogurt	

In a bowl, combine tomatoes, oil, ketchup, salt, sugar, basil, and pepper. Set aside.

In a 6 qt/6 L casserole, combine beans, potatoes, carrots, onions, celery, peppers, and eggplant. Add tomato mixture to vegetables. Cover and bake in oven for 1 1/2 hours, basting vegetables with juices every 30 minutes.

Remove casserole from oven and add zucchini. Return to oven and bake uncovered for 20 to 30 minutes more or until potatoes are tender. Stir gently before serving. Top each portion with yogurt, if desired. This can be kept for up to one week in the refrigerator.

Serves 8.

Nutritional analysis per serving:
134 Calories   6 g protein   2 g fat   28 g carbohydrate   0 mg cholesterol   6 g fiber

UBC SALAD BOWL
Marilyn Husdon

A delicious light summer salad. Artichoke hearts can be expensive, but help turn an ordinary tossed salad into something special.

4 cups	**iceberg lettuce, broken**	**1 L**
1 can	**artichoke hearts (14 oz/398 mL), quartered**	**1 can**
1 can	**tomatoes (16 oz/454 mL), drained and coarsely chopped**	**1 can**
1/2 tsp	**seasoned salt**	**2 mL**
1/4 cup	**packaged rye croutons**	**50 mL**
1/3 cup	**bottled low calorie Italian dressing**	**75 mL**

Place lettuce in large bowl. Arrange artichoke hearts and tomatoes on top. Sprinkle with seasoned salt and croutons. Toss with salad dressing.

Serves 6.

Nutritional analysis per serving:
55 Calories   3 g protein   1 g fat   11 g carbohydrate   1 mg cholesterol

---

Bottled low calorie or fat free Italian dressing is a great marinade for vegetables. Pour dressing over halved mushrooms, broccoli and cauliflower florets, and halved cherry tomatoes. Marinate overnight.

GOURMET TOSSED SALAD

Traditional salad fixings are iceberg lettuce, tomatoes and cucumbers, but the tossed salad has undergone a transformation into a splendid array of crisp colourful vegetables.

The **basic ingredient** is still lettuce – but the varieties available are endless. Use mild lettuce or other greens such as Romaine, leaf, spinach, or butter lettuce for the bulk of your salad. To complement these, add small amounts of any one or more of the sharper flavoured greens to make a more interesting salad. Try radicchio, watercress, curly endive, Belgian endive, arugula, dandelion greens, escarole, mustard greens and chard.

For **colour** and **texture** add any combination of yellow tomatoes, thinly sliced red onion, coloured peppers, peeled and slivered jicama, chopped fennel and sliced mushrooms. Fruit such as orange sections, raspberries, sliced strawberries, mango pieces and papaya chunks add a "sweet" touch and help "dress" up the salad with less dressing. Even canned vegetables such as artichoke hearts, hearts of palm, baby corn and water chestnuts give more life to simple lettuce.

Low fat bottled dressing is the easiest way to dress the salad especially with so many varieties available. However, making your own dressing is really quite simple. Main ingredients are oil, vinegar, and a seasoning. Use a blend of 3 parts vinegar to 1 part oil. To olive or canola oil, add balsamic, wine, fruit flavoured, herbed or rice vinegar. Season it with herbs and spices to suit your taste.

For a final touch, choose a topping. Try low fat croutons, a sprinkling of toasted sliced almonds or a spoonful of sesame seeds.

CURRIED RICE SALAD
Maria Ragone

This is a great dish for buffets in that it can be made ahead of time and chilled. The orange juice adds an interesting tang to the flavour. The amount of curry can be adjusted to suit your taste.

2 cups	cooked long grain rice, cooled	500 mL
4	green onions, sliced	4
1	celery stalk, sliced	1
1/2 cup	carrots, diced	125 mL
1/4 cup	raisins	50 mL
1/4 cup	peanuts, chopped	50 mL
1/4 cup	orange juice	50 mL
1	garlic clove, crushed and minced	1
1/2 tsp	curry powder	2 mL
1 Tbsp	apricot jam	15 mL
1/4 tsp	dry mustard	1 mL
1 Tbsp	olive oil	15 mL
	salt and pepper to taste	

Combine cooked rice, green onions, celery, carrots, raisins, and peanuts. Set aside. Whisk together orange juice, garlic, curry powder, apricot jam, dry mustard and olive oil. Pour over rice mixture and toss. Add salt and pepper to taste.

Serves 4.

Nutritional analysis per serving:
280 Calories   6 g protein   8 g fat   46 g carbohydrate   0 mg cholesterol

All nuts except chestnuts are high in fat. Adding just a small amount will give you that "nutty" flavour without giving you too much fat.

HERBED POTATO SALAD
Shauna Ratner

Traditional potato salads can be high in fat and cholesterol. Vinaigrette dressings provide a new twist to an old favourite without all the extra fat.

2 lb	**small new red potatoes**	**900 g**
1	**red pepper, diced**	**1**
1	**green pepper, diced**	**1**
1	**yellow pepper, diced**	**1**
1/2 cup	**green onions, chopped**	**125 mL**
1/4 cup	**fresh dill, chopped**	**50 mL**
1/4 cup	**fresh parsley, chopped**	**50 mL**
3 Tbsp	**coarse grained Dijon mustard**	**45 mL**
5 Tbsp	**red wine vinegar**	**75 mL**
3 Tbsp	**olive oil**	**45 mL**

salt and pepper to taste

In a medium saucepan, cover whole potatoes with cold water. Bring to a boil and let simmer until soft. Drain and let cool. Cut potatoes into halves or quarters.

In large mixing bowl, stir together pepper, potatoes, and herbs.

In a small jar or glass, whisk together mustard, oil, vinegar, salt and pepper. Pour over vegetables and mix well. Chill before serving.

Serves 8.

Nutritional analysis per seving:
126 calories   4 g protein   6 g fat   17 g carbohydrate   0 mg cholesterol

Most salads really have no set recipe. Any number of ingredients in varying amounts can be used to suit your palate and meet your nutritional needs. So, use your imagination and customize the salad recipes to your liking.

LAYERED SPRING SALAD
Ted Croasdell

This colourful salad is perfect as part of a spring buffet. The citrus flavours and the cucumbers complement one another and produce a delicious combination. You can reduce the fat content further by using fat free mayonnaise.

1 pkg	lime gelatin dessert powder (3 oz/85 g)	1 pkg
1 cup	low fat mayonnaise	250 mL
1/2 cup	celery, diced	125 mL
1/2 cup	cucumber, diced	125 mL
1/4 cup	slivered almonds	50 mL
2	green onions, finely chopped	2
1 cup	1% cottage cheese	250 mL
2 cups	tomato juice	500 mL
1 pkg	lemon gelatin dessert powder (3 oz/85 g)	1 pkg
1 Tbsp	vinegar	15 mL

Dissolve lime gelatin powder in one cup boiling water. Cool until partially congealed. Beat until foamy. Add mayonnaise and beat again. Add celery, cucumber, almonds, onion and cottage cheese. Mix gently and put into mold. Chill until firm. Heat tomato juice to boiling and add lemon gelatin powder and vinegar. Stir until dissolved. Pour over chilled lime mixture. Chill until firm. Unmold onto serving platter.

Serves 10.

Nutritional analysis per serving:
174 calories   6 g protein   8 g fat   21 g carbohydrate   1 mg cholesterol

ANTIPASTA SALAD
Anne Swonnell

Add sliced black olives, artichoke hearts and sundried tomatoes to give this salad a Mediterranean touch. If you add canned tuna, you can turn this into a "light meal."

1/3 cup	water	75 mL
1/3 cup	red wine vinegar	75 mL
2 Tbsp	olive oil	30 mL
1 pkg	Knorr™ Vegetable Soup mix	1 pkg
1	garlic clove, minced	1
1 Tbsp	fresh basil, chopped	15 mL
3 cups	cooked pasta	750 mL

In a small saucepan, bring water and vinegar to a boil. Remove from the stove and add the vegetable soup mix. Stir until dissolved. Add the garlic, basil, and pasta and mix well. Cover and chill before serving.

Makes 3 cups/750 mL.

Nutritional analysis per 1/2 cup/125 mL:
143 calories   3 g protein   5 g fat   21 g carbohydrate   0 mg cholesterol

Packaged soup mixes are usually high in sodium, so use them in small amounts. If you're using them as a soup base, add extra water and lots of vegetables.

BRUNCHES AND LIGHT MEALS

There's been a move towards eating smaller and more frequent meals. Some call it "grazing"...with many of us opting for lighter foods. The days of heavy gravies, meats and potatoes are fewer and far between. Whether it's a hot summer day, a special brunch or just a busy evening these light meal ideas are perfect.

Here are some suggestions for preparing lighter meals:

• Add canned tuna, salmon, sliced ham, chicken or garbanzo beans to a salad. Use a variety of greens to keep it interesting and toss it with a light dressing. Serve it with a hearty fresh bread or try some of the flavoured breads now available such as tomato, olive, foccacia or herb.

• Breakfast foods like pancakes and french toast don't just have to be for breakfast. Use only egg whites or a mixture of whole eggs and extra whites for less dietary cholesterol. Serve these for lunch or dinner along with yogurt and fruit.

• Remember to include plenty of vegetables, even with lighter meals. Add extra vegetables to casseroles to add more bulk.

• Use as little fat as possible in cooking.

• Balance out your day when planning a special meal. If you know that you will be eating more then, make your other meals lighter.

SALMON AND PASTA SALAD

Judy Miletech

This salad is perfect for a light meal on a hot summer day. For a "zestier" salad add more herbs.

1/2 cup	plain low fat yogurt	125 mL
2 Tbsp	calorie reduced mayonnaise	30 mL
2 Tbsp	lemon juice	30 mL
2 tsp	fresh basil, chopped	10 mL
1/4 tsp	oregano	1 mL
	salt and pepper to taste	
2 cups	macaroni, cooked	500 mL
1 can	salmon (7 1/2 oz/213 g)	1 can
1 cup	celery, chopped	250 mL
1	red pepper, chopped	1
1	red onion, diced	1

In medium size mixing bowl combine yogurt, mayonnaise, lemon juice, basil, oregano, salt and pepper. Stir and set aside.

In another bowl mix together remaining ingredients. Add to the yogurt mixture. Toss to coat the pasta. Refrigerate until ready to serve. Mix well before serving.

Serves 4.

Nutritional analysis per serving:
270 calories   16 g protein   9 g fat   32 g carbohydrate   15 mg cholesterol

You can always substitute dry herbs if fresh aren't available. However, it's always more flavourful to use fresh, such as basil, dill, oregano and parsley.

CHICKEN SALAD VERONIQUE
Claudette Bertholet

Grapes and lemon yogurt combine together well to give a refreshing taste to this chicken salad. This is delicious with or without the frosted grape clusters.

2 cups	chicken, cooked and cubed	500 mL
1 cup	seedless green grapes, halved	250 mL
1/4 cup	toasted slivered almonds (optional)	50 mL
1/2 cup	celery, chopped	125 mL
3 Tbsp	onion, chopped	45 mL
1/2 tsp	celery salt	2 mL
1/4 cup	calorie reduced mayonnaise	50 mL
1/3 cup	lemon yogurt	75 mL
1 Tbsp	white wine or 1 tsp/2 mL lemon juice	15 mL
1/2 tsp	prepared mustard	2 mL
	frosted grape clusters (see below)	
	leaf lettuce	

In a medium size bowl mix chicken, grapes, almonds (if using), celery, onion and celery salt and set aside. In a small bowl mix together mayonnaise, yogurt, wine or lemon juice and mustard. Fold mayonnaise mixture into chicken. Refrigerate until ready to serve.

Before serving prepare frosted grape clusters if using (see below). Arrange lettuce leaves on individual plates and spoon chicken mixture onto leaves. Garnish with frosted grape clusters.

Serves 6.

Frosted Grape Clusters

6	seedless grapes clusters	6
1	egg white	1
1 pkg	lime flavoured gelatin (3 oz/85 g)	1 pkg

Brush grape clusters with egg white. Sprinkle with lime gelatin. Dry on a rack.

Nutritional analysis per serving:
183 calories   17 g protein   9 g fat   10 g carbohydrate   40 mg cholesterol

STEAK LOVERS' SALAD
John Harrop

This salad is a meal in itself with small strips of meat surrounded by lots of fresh vegetables. It's a great way to use up leftover barbecued beef.

3 cups	fresh green beans	750 mL
1 tsp	garlic, minced	5 mL
8 – 10 oz	lean beef, sirloin	225 – 300 g
2 tsp	oil	10 mL
1	small red onion, sliced	1
4 cups	butter lettuce	1 L
2 cups	spinach, raw	500 mL
3	large mushrooms, sliced	3

Steam green beans until tender. Heat oil in nonstick pan. Sauté green beans and garlic over medium heat. Remove beans and sauté onions in the same pan, until cooked. Broil steak to desired doneness (or barbecue) and slice into thin strips.

Wash lettuce and spinach and spread on serving platter. Arrange steak, green beans, onions and sliced mushrooms on top. Pour dressing over platter and serve.

Serves 3 as a main course.

Salad Dressing

2 Tbsp	olive oil	30 mL
1 Tbsp	lemon juice	15 mL
1/2 tsp	Dijon mustard	2 mL
	salt and pepper to taste	

Stir all ingredients together.

Nutritional analysis per serving:
332 calories   30 g protein   17 g fat   17 g carbohydrate   54 mg cholesterol

CALZONE
Sylvia Loewen

Calzone is like a "folded over pizza". This meatless version takes a little work but the outcome is delicious. You could add chopped zucchini, peppers or any vegetables you desire.

Part 1 – Dough

1 Tbsp	**dry yeast**	**15 mL**
1 tsp	**sugar**	**5 mL**
1/2 cup	**warm water**	**125 mL**
2 cups	**whole wheat flour**	**500 mL**
2 -3 cups	**white flour**	**500 – 750 mL**
1 tsp	**salt**	**5 mL**
1 cup	**skim milk**	**250 mL**
2 Tbsp	**oil**	**30 mL**

Place yeast, sugar, water in a large bowl and let stand for 5 minutes. Add whole wheat flour, 1 cup/250 mL of the white flour and salt. Mix well. Add milk and oil, and mix thoroughly adding more flour as needed until dough is smooth and forms a ball. Cover and let rise until dough doubles in size, about 1 hour. (For a short cut, use pre-made pizza dough or frozen bread dough)

Part 2 – Tomato Sauce

1 can	**tomatoes (19 oz/540 mL)**	**1 can**
1 can	**tomato paste (7 oz/175 mL)**	**1 can**
1 -2 tsp	**oregano**	**5 – 10 mL**
1 tsp	**basil**	**5 mL**

Put all ingredients in a small pot and bring to a gentle boil. Let simmer for 45 minutes. Add more spices to suit your taste. (For a short cut use bottled pizza sauce).

Part 3 – Filling

1 cup	1% cottage cheese	250 mL
8	mushrooms, sliced	8
1	onion, chopped	1

Steam or microwave mushrooms and onions until soft. Drain liquid, if any. Add the cottage cheese and mix. Set aside.

Putting it all together:
Punch down the dough and divide it into 16 pieces. Roll each piece into a flat circle and let rise for 10 minutes. Mix together 1 Tbsp/15 mL olive oil and 1 minced garlic clove. Brush each circle with the garlic oil. Spread about 1 1/2 Tbsp/20 mL of tomato sauce over half the dough, leaving an edge of 1/2 in/2 cm. Spread 1 1/2 Tbsp/20 mL of cottage cheese filling over the sauce. Fold in half and pinch top to bottom. Brush top with garlic oil and salt lightly if desired. Place on cookie sheet. Bake at 400°F for 10 – 15 minutes.

Makes 16.

Nutritional analysis per calzone:
189 calories   7 g protein   3 g fat   33 g carbohydrate   1 mg cholesterol

Restaurant pizza is usually oozing with fat! Make your own at home using ready made pizza crusts, topped with tomato sauce and vegetables of your choice. Try sautéed mushrooms, onions and red peppers for a super flavour combination. Sprinkle with just a little grated low fat mozzarella cheese.

SALMON BROCCOLI QUICHE
Evelyn Priest

This is much lower in fat and cholesterol than traditional quiche. You can use leftover cooked fresh salmon instead of the canned.

1 Tbsp	soft margarine	15 mL
1	medium onion, chopped	1
1 cup	broccoli, chopped	250 mL
1 cup	skim milk	250 mL
1 cup	egg substitute	250 mL
3/4 cup	Bisquick™ baking mix	200 mL
1/2 tsp	salt	2 mL
1/4 tsp	dill weed	1 mL
1/4 tsp	pepper	1 mL
1 can	salmon (7 1/2 oz/213 g), drained and flaked	1 can
1 cup	part skim mozzarella, grated	250 mL

In nonstick frying pan melt margarine. Add onion and sauté until tender. Stir in broccoli and cook for 1 minute. Set aside.

In mixing bowl beat together egg substitute, milk, Bisquick™ and seasonings. Add salmon, cheese and broccoli mixture and mix. Spray 10 in/26 cm pie plate or quiche pan with nonstick spray and pour in salmon mixture.

Bake at 400°F for 30 – 35 minutes or until a knife inserted close to the centre comes out clean. Let stand for 5 minutes before serving.

Serves 8.

Nutritional analysis per serving:
232 calories   19 g protein   11 g fat   15 g carbohydrate   18 mg cholesterol

One egg yolk has 214 mg of cholesterol, but egg whites are virtually cholesterol and fat free! Egg substitutes can be used in place of whole eggs, or 2 egg whites can be used in place of 1 whole egg in most recipes.

OVERNIGHT TUNA CASSEROLE
Theresa Florkow

This casserole is a tasty timesaver. You can mix the ingredients together the night before and leave it in the refrigerator until just before you are ready to cook it. Cut up carrot and celery sticks and fresh fruit while the casserole cooks for 20 minutes. Voila Dinner!

1 can	lowfat cream of celery soup (10 oz/284 mL)	1 can
10 oz	skim milk	284 mL
1 can	tuna in water (6 1/2 oz/184 g)	1 can
1 cup	elbow macaroni, uncooked	250 mL
1 cup	frozen peas	250mL
1/2 cup	onion, chopped	125 mL
1/2 cup	part skim cheddar cheese, grated	125 mL

Whisk soup and milk together in a 2 qt/2 L microwavable casserole dish until well blended. Stir in remaining ingredients except for 2 Tbsp/30 mL of the grated cheese. Cover and refrigerate for at least 12 hours or overnight.

Microwave casserole covered on high for 17 minutes or until mixture is hot and bubbly. Sprinkle with remaining cheese and let stand uncovered for 5 minutes.

Serves 4.

Nutritional analysis per serving:
339 calories   28 g protein   10 g fat   35 g carbohydrate   29 mg cholesterol

When buying canned tuna make sure it's canned in water or vegetable broth. Tuna canned in oil adds at least an extra 5 grams of fat!

TOFU QUICHE
David Softly

This recipe is well worth the effort. It is a light, but surprisingly flavourful quiche. The flavour can be varied by substituting your favourite vegetables and fresh herbs. It is a great luncheon dish accompanied by a crisp green salad with a zesty dressing.

Part 1 – Pastry

1 cup	whole wheat flour	250 mL
1/4 cup	margarine	50 mL
1/4 cup	water	50 mL
1/2 tsp	salt	2 mL

Mix together flour and salt. Blend in margarine by hand until mixture is crumbly. Add enough water, 1 Tbsp/15 mL at a time to form pastry into a ball. Roll the pastry out on a floured surface and place into a 9 in/23 cm pie plate or springform pan. Set aside.

Part 2 – Filling

1	onion, diced	1
2 cups	mushrooms, sliced	500 mL
1	red or yellow pepper, diced	1
2 cups	broccoli, chopped	500 mL
1 Tbsp	olive oil	15 mL
	garlic powder to taste	
1 pkg	medium firm tofu (16 oz/454 g)	1 pkg
2 Tbsp	whole wheat flour	30 mL
2 Tbsp	parmesan cheese, grated	30 mL
2 Tbsp	lemon juice	30 mL
2 Tbsp	olive oil	30 mL
1/2 tsp	garlic powder	2 mL
1 tsp	oregano	5 mL
1 tsp	salt	5 mL

Sauté onion in oil. Add pepper and mushrooms. Lower heat and sprinkle with garlic powder. Add broccoli. Cover and steam vegetables for 3 minutes or until vegetables are tender, adding water if necessary. Remove from heat, drain excess liquid and set aside.

In medium size bowl, mash tofu with a fork. Add flour, cheese, lemon juice, olive oil and seasonings. Stir thoroughly. Add prepared vegetables and mix well.

Pour the filling into the pastry shell. Garnish, if you wish, with tomato slices and strips of pepper. Bake at 350°F for 40 – 50 minutes.

Serves 8.

Nutritional analysis per serving:
240 calories   12 g protein   11 g fat   28 g carbohydrate   1 mg cholesterol

With only 4 grams of fat per 3 oz/90 g portion, tofu is a great substitute for meat. Tofu comes in all kinds of forms and textures – prepackaged or fresh, firm or soft and plain or flavoured. Choose the tofu that suits your palate.

SALMON AND SPINACH GRATIN
Lynn Hoefsloot

Canned tuna or crab can be used in place of the salmon.

1 pkg	frozen chopped spinach (10 oz/300 g), thawed	1 pkg
1 tsp	soft margarine	5 mL
1 cup	mushrooms, sliced	250 mL
1 Tbsp	soft margarine	15 mL
1 cup	skim milk, hot	250 mL
2 Tbsp	flour	30 mL
2 Tbsp	green onions, chopped	30 mL
1 can	pink salmon (7.5 oz/213 g)	1 can
	pepper to taste	
2 Tbsp	fresh brown bread crumbs	30 mL
2 Tbsp	parmesan cheese, grated	30 mL
1 Tbsp	fresh parsley, chopped	15 mL

Drain water out of the spinach by squeezing. Spread spinach in the bottom of an 8 in/20 cm baking dish and set aside.

Melt 1 tsp/5 mL margarine in a small nonstick frying pan. Add the mushrooms and sauté over medium heat, until browned. Spread the mushrooms over the spinach. In the same nonstick pan melt 1 tbsp/15 mL margarine. Stir in flour and sauté for 1 minute over medium heat, stirring continuously. Add the hot milk and whisk until mixture simmers and is smooth and thickened. Stir in green onions and pepper to taste. Mash the salmon together with the bones and juice, and add to the milk mixture. Stir thoroughly. Add to the baking dish and set aside.

For the topping, combine breadcrumbs, parmesan cheese and parsley and sprinkle over top of salmon mixture. Microwave on high for 3 minutes or bake in oven at 350°F for 5 minutes until heated through. Brown under broiler until golden.

Serves 4.

Nutritional analysis per serving:
204 calories   16 g protein   11 g fat   12 g carbohydrate   17 mg cholesterol

TUNA MUFFINS

Evelyn Chaffey

Don't let the name fool you. These are "mini tuna casseroles" baked in muffin tins, and taste great.

2 cups	brown rice, cooked	500 mL
3 Tbsp	parmesan cheese, grated	45 mL
1/4 cup	green or white onion chopped	50 mL
1 Tbsp	parsley flakes	15 mL
1 Tbsp	lemon juice	15 mL
1 can	tuna in water (6 1/2 oz/184 g)	1 can
3	egg whites	3
5 Tbsp	skim milk yogurt	75 mL
2 tsp	tamari or soy sauce	10 mL

In medium size mixing bowl combine all ingredients together except egg whites. In another bowl beat egg whites until stiff and fold into tuna mixture.

Spray muffin tins with nonstick spray or paper-line. Spoon muffin mixture generously into muffin tins, heaping to form muffin shape. Bake at 375°F for 35 – 40 minutes.

Makes 6 muffins.

Nutritional analysis per muffin:
146 calories   14 g protein   2 g fat   18 g carbohydrate   9 mg cholesterol

Parmesan cheese is still 22% milk fat and should be used sparingly. Even a small amount can enhance the flavour of an otherwise mild dish.

GREEK STYLE TUNA SANDWICH
John Peters

Try making these on toasted bagels or multigrain English muffins.

1 Tbsp	low calorie mayonnaise	15 mL
1 tsp	lemon juice	5 mL
1/4 tsp	oregano	1 mL
1 can	flaked tuna in water (3 oz/100 g)	1 can
2 Tbsp	1% cottage cheese	30 mL
1 Tbsp	green onion, chopped	15 mL
4	thick slices Italian bread, toasted	4
1	large tomato, sliced	1
2 Tbsp	feta cheese, crumbled	30 mL
	pepper to taste	

Stir together mayonnaise, lemon juice and oregano in a medium size bowl. Drain tuna and add to mayonnaise mixture. Mix in cottage cheese and green onion. Divide tuna evenly among the 4 slices of toast. Top each with 2 – 3 tomato slices and sprinkle of feta cheese and pepper.

To heat sandwiches, place on a microwavable safe plate and heat on high for 30 – 45 seconds or until cheese is melted; or arrange on a broiler pan and broil 4 in/10 cm from the heat for 3 minutes until cheese is golden.

Makes 2 servings.

Nutritional analysis per serving:
354 calories   22 g protein   9 g fat   46 g carbohydrate   25 mg cholesterol

"Buttering" bread for sandwiches is just a habit. Most sandwich fillings provide enough flavour and moisture without butter or margarine. Better spreads are mustards, cranberry sauce, salsa, horseradish and chutney.

VEGETABLE QUESADILLA
Frances Johnson

Quesadilla can be described as "Mexican sandwiches". Flour tortillas filled with melted cheese and vegetables are a nice change from regular sandwiches. The jalapeno pepper adds a delectable nip.

2	coloured peppers, thinly sliced	2
1	fresh jalapeno pepper, chopped	1
1	onion, thinly sliced	1
1	garlic clove, minced	1
1 tsp	oil	5 mL
1/4 tsp	salt	1 mL
2 Tbsp	fresh cilantro or parsley, chopped	30 mL
12	flour tortillas (6 in/15 cm)	12
6 oz	7% mf cheddar style cheese, grated	175 g

In nonstick pan, sauté peppers, jalapeno, onion and garlic with oil until vegetables are soft. Add salt and cilantro or parsley and mix.

Spread 1/6 of mixture onto each of 6 tortillas. Sprinkle each of the 6 tortillas with cheese. Top each with the remaining plain tortilla to make 6 "sandwiches".

Place on baking sheet in single layer. Cover with aluminum foil and bake in preheated oven at 350°F for 10 minutes or until cheese is melted.

Cut into quarters. Serve warm.

Serves 6.

Nutritional analysis per serving:
290 calories   13 g protein   6 g fat   47 g carbohydrate   27 mg cholesterol

Like sandwiches, quesadillas can have any number of fillings, limited only by your imagination. Try using refried beans with jalapeno and cheese; artichoke hearts, sundried tomatoes and cheese; or for a "meatier" meal add diced chicken, vegetables and cheese.

OAT PANCAKES
Mary Sugiyama

Serve these with a mixture of fresh berries, or top them with any fresh fruit in season and low fat yogurt.

1 cup	flour	250 mL
1 Tbsp	sugar	15 mL
2 tsp	baking powder	10 mL
1/2 tsp	salt	2 mL
1/2 cup	rolled oats	125 mL
1 1/4 cups	skim milk	300 mL
2	egg whites, whisked	2
1 Tbsp	apple juice	15 mL

In a mixing bowl combine flour, sugar, baking powder and salt. Mix well and set aside. Soak rolled oats in milk and let sit for 5 minutes. Combine beaten egg whites and apple juice together and add to oatmeal. Gradually add oat mixture to dry ingredients, stirring until just blended. If batter is too thick add a little more milk.

Heat nonstick skillet over medium heat. Drop batter into skillet from large spoon and cook until surface is full of bubbles and underside is golden brown. Flip over and cook until other side is lightly browned.

Makes 10 – 3 in/8 cm pancakes.

Nutritional analysis per pancake:
96 calories   4 g protein   1 g fat   18 g carbohydrate   1 mg cholesterol

Pancakes themselves are a great breakfast choice. It's the butter or margarine on top that can add so much fat. Leave off the butter and use your imagination for pancake toppers. Some suggestions are: fruit compote, French vanilla yogurt (low fat, of course), cinnamon sugar, applesauce or fruit flavoured syrups.

MEATLESS MEALS AND GRAINS

In the last few years, there has been a general trend towards eating less meat, and more grains and legumes. Meatless meals provide the ideal combination for healthy eating. Not only are these vegetarian type meals flavourful and interesting, they offer less saturated fat and cholesterol, and more fiber than our traditional meat-centered meals. Combinations of beans, split peas, lentils, tofu, all kinds of grains and pasta, and low fat dairy products can provide you with the protein you need. Keep in mind, though, that it is not necessary to eliminate meats entirely from your diet to reap the benefits of vegetarian style eating – just try to include some meatless meals in your meal plan each week.

Here are some suggestions for preparing meatless meals:

• All dried beans other than lentils and split peas need to be soaked before cooking. Soak in 3 to 4 times as much water as beans for at least 8 hours. To cook, bring to a boil, reduce the heat, and simmer until tender, usually up to 2 to 3 hours.

• Add canned kidney or navy beans and noodles to any vegetable soup to make a meal in itself.

• Try commercial vegetarian patties instead of meat patties to make hamburgers. Include all the regular "trimmings" such as lettuce, tomatoes, onions, and a little light mayonnaise.

• Use low fat cheese instead of regular cheese wherever possible. When using a high fat cheese such as parmesan, use just a sprinkle to give you the flavour you want.

• Add tofu to a vegetable stir fry for extra protein. Prepare stir fried vegetables as usual, but just before the vegetables are done, add cubed tofu. Stir fry gently until the tofu is hot and the vegetables are cooked.

• Use nuts and seeds sparingly since they are so high in fat. Using just a small amount will give a touch of flavour without too much fat.

• Add garbanzo beans to a vegetable salad for added protein.

• For a quick lunch, serve hummus with pita bread and minestrone soup.

• Remember to use very little oil and margarine in preparing vegetarian meals.

HANNELORE'S CHILI
Hannelore Vannetta

This is a very flavourful vegetarian chili. If you prefer a thicker chili, a little flour and water can be added to thicken it.

1 1/2 cups	onion, chopped	375 mL
2	green peppers, chopped	2
2	celery stalks, chopped	2
1	zucchini, sliced	1
4	garlic cloves, minced	4
2 Tbsp	oil	30 mL
2 cans	tomatoes (28 oz/796 mL)	2 cans
1 can	kidney beans (14 oz/398 mL)	1 can
1 can	brown beans (14 oz/398 mL)	1 can
2 cups	mushrooms, sliced	500 mL
1/4 cup	vinegar	50 mL
1	bay leaf	1
1 Tbsp	chili powder	15 mL
1 Tbsp	parsley	15 mL
1 1/2 tsp	basil	7 mL
1 1/2 tsp	oregano	7 mL
1 1/2 tsp	pepper	7 mL
3 "squirts"	Worcestershire sauce	3 "squirts"

Sauté onion, green pepper, celery, zucchini, and garlic in oil until tender. Add tomatoes and beans including liquid, mushrooms, vinegar, and spices. Simmer for 1 hour. Remove bay leaf before serving. Thicken, if desired.

Serves 10.

Nutritional analysis per serving:
192 Calories   8 g protein   4 g fat   31 g carbohydrate   0 mg cholesterol

Most "red" sauces such as salsa, barbecue, ketchup, tomato and Worcestershire sauces are low in fat and are great to spice up your meals.

RED LENTIL STEW
Glen Black

Use red lentils to prepare this stew as they have a milder flavour. If you like, add zucchini or peppers, or any other of your favourite vegetables.

3 cups	red lentils, uncooked	750 mL
7 cups	water	1.7 L
1	vegetable or chicken bouillon cube	1
1	onion, chopped	1
1/2 cup	celery, chopped	125 mL
1/2 cup	carrots, chopped	125 mL
1 can	tomatoes (14 oz/398 mL)	1 can
1	garlic clove, minced	1
2 tsp	salt	10 mL
1 tsp	pepper	5 mL
1 tsp	oregano	5 mL
1 tsp	oil	5 mL

Heat oil in a large soup pot over medium heat. Sauté onion, garlic, celery, and carrots for 2 minutes. Add remaining ingredients and bring to a boil. Reduce heat and simmer uncovered for 40 minutes or until lentils are tender. Season with additional spices as desired.

Serves 8.

Nutritional analysis per serving:
207 Calories   15 g protein   1 g fat   38 g carbohydrate   0 mg cholesterol   9 g fiber

Lentils are a good source of protein and high in fiber.

LENTIL AND BARLEY STEW
Roy Williams

Serve this flavourful vegetarian stew with a tossed salad and fresh rolls for a quick simple meal.

1/2 lb	red lentils, uncooked	225 g
1 cup	pearl barley, uncooked	250 mL
4 cups	water	1 L
2 Tbsp	oil	30 mL
2	large onions, diced	2
2	large carrots, sliced	2
2	potatoes, peeled and diced	2
1 cup	celery, chopped	250 mL
1/2 cup	turnip, diced	125 mL
1 can	tomatoes (28 oz/796 mL)	1 can
2 tsp	salt	10 mL
1/2 tsp	pepper	2 mL
1/2 tsp	thyme	2 mL
1	bay leaf	1

Cover lentils with 4 cups/1 L water and boil 2 minutes. Remove from heat and let stand 1 hour. Rinse barley with cold water and set aside.

Heat oil in large Dutch oven. Add onions and cook for 3 minutes, stirring constantly. Add lentils with water used for soaking and remaining ingredients. Bring to a boil. Reduce heat, cover, and simmer for 2 hours, stirring frequently. Add more water, if necessary to keep from sticking. Mixture will be thick.

Makes 6 large servings.

Nutritional analysis per serving:
436 Calories   15 g protein   6 g fat   86 g carbohydrate   0 mg cholesterol   13 g fiber

BAKED PENNE
Frances Johnson

This recipe makes 8 very generous servings and is a great change from spaghetti or lasagna. Prepare it ahead of time along with marinated vegetables.

1/2 Tbsp	oil	8 mL
3 cups	mushrooms, sliced	750 mL
1	onion, chopped	1
4	garlic cloves, minced	4
1/3 cup	flour	75 mL
3 cups	skim milk	750 mL
2 pkg	frozen spinach (10 oz/300 g)	2 pkg
1 can	diced tomatoes, undrained (28 oz/796 mL)	1 can
1 1/2 tsp	basil	7 mL
1/2 tsp	oregano	2 mL
1 1/2 tsp	salt	7 mL
3/4 tsp	pepper	3 mL
1 lb	penne pasta, uncooked	454 g
3/4 cup	grated parmesan cheese	200 mL

In a large saucepan, heat oil. Cook mushrooms, onion and garlic until softened. Sprinkle flour over top and cook, stirring for 1 minute. Gradually whisk in milk and cook, stirring until hot and thickened. Squeeze spinach dry and chop. Add to sauce along with the tomatoes, herbs, salt and pepper. Cook stirring until heated through. Set aside.

Cook pasta in boiling water until tender but firm. Drain and rinse under cold water. Drain and add to the sauce. Toss well. Spoon half into 13x9 in/33x23 cm baking dish. Sprinkle with half of the parmesan cheese. Repeat layers. Bake uncovered in 350°F oven for 35 – 40 minutes or until heated through.

Serves 8.

Nutritional analysis per serving:
373 Calories   19 g protein   6 g fat   64 g carbohydrate   9 mg cholesterol

You might call grains the main powerhouses for our diet, providing us with the carbohydrates that give us the energy we need. They're not fattening as many believe...it's the spreads and sauces that you need to watch.

RICOTTA LASAGNA ROLLS
John Peters

This meatless version of lasagna is delicious. For a shortcut, you can use ready-made spaghetti sauce instead of making the sauce from scratch. The individual rolls make serving very easy for a buffet.

1	small onion, chopped	1
2	garlic cloves, minced	2
1 can	tomato sauce (15 oz/450 mL)	1 can
1 Tbsp	sugar	15 mL
1/2 tsp	basil	2 mL
dash	pepper	dash
1 pkg	frozen spinach (10 oz/300 g), thawed and well drained	1 pkg
1 cup	part skim ricotta cheese	250 mL
2 Tbsp	parmesan cheese, grated	30 mL
1/4 tsp	nutmeg	1 mL
8	lasagna noodles, cooked	8

Sauce:
Spray saucepan with nonstick spray, and cook onion and garlic until tender. Add tomato sauce, sugar, basil, and pepper. Bring to boil. Reduce heat and simmer uncovered for 15 minutes, stirring frequently.

Filling:
Combine spinach, ricotta cheese, Parmesan cheese, and nutmeg.

To assemble:
Spread about 3 Tbsp/45mL of the spinach mixture on each lasagna noodle. Roll up noodle and place seam side down into 2 qt/2 L square baking dish. Repeat with remaining spinach mixture and noodles. Spoon sauce over lasagna rolls in dish. Bake in 350°F oven for 20 minutes or until heated through, and sauce is bubbly.

Serves 4 (2 rolls per serving).

Nutritional analysis per serving:
410 Calories   20 g protein   7 g fat   68 g carbohydrate   21 mg cholesterol

When making traditional pan style lasagna, you can buy precooked noodles to cut down on the preparation time. You'll need to add a little extra liquid to the sauce.

PASTA WITH EGGPLANT TOMATO SAUCE

Shauna Ratner

You won't even miss the meat in this hearty tomato sauce. This dish is much lower in fat than usual since the eggplant is not fried. It's great served over rotini, but you can use any shaped noodles.

1	**small eggplant, diced**	1
1/2 Tbsp	**olive oil**	7 mL
2	**garlic cloves, minced**	2
1	**small onion, chopped**	1
1 cup	**mushrooms, sliced**	250 mL
1 can	**tomatoes, chopped (28 oz/796 mL)**	1 can
1/4 cup	**red wine**	50 mL
2 Tbsp	**fresh basil, chopped**	30 mL
1/2 lb	**rotinti**	225 g
1/4 cup	**parmesan cheese, grated**	50 mL
	pinch sugar	
	red pepper flakes to taste	

Heat olive oil in medium size saucepan. Sauté onions and garlic until tender. Add eggplant and mushrooms and sauté for 2 minutes (you may want to add some of the liquid from the tomatoes to prevent vegetables from sticking to the pot). Add canned tomatoes, red wine, sugar and a pinch of red pepper flakes and mix well. Bring to a boil and then reduce heat. Let simmer for 1 hour or until eggplant is cooked. Stir in fresh basil and cook for 5 minutes longer. Spice with additional pepper flakes to taste.

In a large pot of boiling water cook pasta until al dente. Drain pasta. Top pasta with sauce and a sprinkling of parmesan cheese.

Makes 4 servings.

Nutritional analysis per serving:
341 calories   13 g protein   5 g fat   60 g carbohydrate   5 mg cholesterol

LENTIL BROWN RICE CASSEROLE
Arlana Leech

The brown rice and lentils make a tasty healthy combination in this very simple casserole. Serve with a tossed salad and whole grain rolls for an easy vegetarian meal. Basil, tarragon or a combination of these herbs can be used instead of the parsley.

1/2 cup	brown rice, uncooked	125 mL
1/2 cup	lentils, uncooked	125 mL
1	onion, chopped	1
1 can	tomatoes (14 oz/398 mL)	1 can
1 1/2 cups	water or vegetable broth	375 mL
1	bay leaf	1
1 Tbsp	parsley	15 mL
1/4 cup	low fat mozzarella cheese, grated	50 mL

In a casserole dish, combine all ingredients except cheese. Cover. Cook at 350°F for approximately 1 1/2 hours. Stir 2 to 3 times while cooking, adding more water, if needed. Sprinkle cheese on top and return to oven until cheese is melted.

Serves 4.

Nutritional analysis per serving:
200 Calories   10 g protein   3 g fat   35 g carbohydrate 5 mg cholesterol   5 g fiber

The nutty flavour and firm texture of brown rice comes from the fact that it is unrefined. Hence, it takes about 15 – 30 minutes longer to cook than white rice.

LENTIL LOAF
Joan Wilder

This is a meat loaf minus all that saturated fat and cholesterol!

2 cups	green lentils, dry	500 mL
1/2 cup	onion, chopped	125 mL
1 cup	mushrooms, chopped	250 mL
1/2	green pepper, chopped	1/2
1 cup	almonds, ground	250 mL
1/2 cup	bread crumbs	125 mL
1/2 – 1 cup	vegetable or tomato juice	125 – 250 mL
	salt and pepper to taste	
	tomato slices	

In a saucepan, combine lentils and enough water to cover by at least 1 in/2.5 cm. Bring to a boil, reduce heat and simmer until lentils are cooked, but not mushy, about 20 minutes. Drain. In a mixing bowl, combine lentils, ground almonds, bread crumbs and vegetables. Add enough vegetable juice to make a soft mixture. Season with salt and pepper to taste. Place in casserole dish. Cover with sliced tomatoes. Bake at 350°F for 30 minutes.

Serves 8.

Nutritional analysis per serving:
179 Calories   10 g protein   9 g fat   20 g carbohydrate   0 mg cholesterol   6 g fiber

Endless varieties of meat substitutes are now available. Try incorporating vegetarian burgers, hotdogs, deli meats, and soy cheese into your diet to reduce your saturated fat intake.

LENTIL CASSEROLE
Evelyn Priest

This "meatless" dish is delicious if served with honey mustard or tomato sauce.

1 cup	lentils, dry	250 mL
1/2 cup	walnuts, chopped	125 mL
1	egg (or 2 egg whites)	1
1/2 cup	evaporated skim milk	125 mL
1/2 cup	cornflake crumbs	125 mL
1	large onion, chopped	1
1 tsp	cumin	5 mL
1/2 tsp	thyme	2 mL

In a large pot combine 3 cups/750 mL of water and lentils. Bring to a boil. Reduce the heat and let simmer for 20 minutes or until lentils are tender. Mix all ingredients together. Place in loaf pan sprayed with nonstick spray. Bake uncovered at 350°F for 30 minutes.

Serves 6.

Nutritional analysis per serving:
161 Calories   9 g protein   7 g fat   18 g carbohydrate   33 mg cholesterol   3 g fiber

MEXICAN CASSEROLE
Tom Graham

Make this casserole using any variety of beans such as kidney, northern, black or white beans. If you want to make this ahead of time, just refrigerate or freeze after sprinkling on the cheese, and reheat it when you need it.

1 can	beans (28 oz/796 mL)	1 can
1 tsp	oil	5 mL
1	garlic clove, minced	1
1	green pepper, chopped	1
1	red pepper, chopped	1
1 can	tomatoes (19 oz/540 mL)	1 can
1/4 tsp	cayenne	1 mL
1/2 cup	water	125 mL
1	onion, chopped	1
1 1/2 cups	mushrooms, sliced	375 mL
3/4 cup	brown rice, uncooked	200 mL
1 tsp	chili powder	5 mL
2 tsp	cumin	10 mL
1 cup	low fat mozzarella cheese, shredded	250 mL

In large pot, heat oil and water. Add onion, garlic, mushrooms, and peppers. Simmer until onions are tender. Add rice, beans, tomatoes, chili powder, cumin and cayenne. Cover and simmer for 45 minutes until rice is cooked and most of the liquid is absorbed. Transfer into a baking dish and sprinkle with cheese. Bake at 350°F oven for 15 minutes, or microwave until casserole is hot and cheese is melted.

Serves 6.

Nutritional analysis per serving:
275 Calories   12 g protein   2 g fat   54 g carbohydrate   3 mg cholesterol   12 g fiber

THE MAIN COURSE

"**W**hat's for dinner tonight?"

In response, what comes to mind is the main course – usually the meat, poultry or fish part of the meal. We plan our dinner around the main course or entree, making it the highlight of the meal. Keep in mind that although these foods are a good source of protein, they also contain fat and cholesterol. So, make sure they are a *healthy highlight* of the meal by taking note of the following guidelines:

- Keep meat, chicken and fish portion sizes small. Count on about 3 oz/90 g or a piece about the size of a woman's palm for each serving.
- Choose lean cuts of meat:
    Beef: round, rump, sirloin tip, sirloin
    Pork: tenderloin, loin
    Lamb: leg of lamb
  Usually bony parts of meat such as the rib cuts have more fat.
- Cut off all visible fat from meat and remove the skin from poultry.
- Plan to have fish at least twice per week. Not only is fish lower in saturated fat, it contains omega – 3 fatty acids which may help to reduce your risk for heart disease.
- Include plenty of the "other parts" of the dinner plate – these include potatoes, rice, pasta and vegetables. While keeping your meat portions smaller, you can fill up on these "other parts."
- Try vegetarian meals once in a while. For good ideas, see the "Meatless Meals" section.
- Make sure you use low fat cooking methods. It's best to bake, broil, poach, barbecue, and stir fry meats.
- Leaner meats are often not as tender as other cuts. Marinating will help to tenderize and add extra flavour.
- Use as little extra fat as possible in cooking meats.

BEEF STROGANOFF
Sylvia Loewen

This is a low fat version of an old favourite "comfort food." Skim milk yogurt can be used instead of milk for a creamier sauce. A marinated salad prepared the night before or a tossed salad are quick accompaniments to this hearty dish.

1/2 lb	lean beef	225 g
1 tsp	Worcestershire sauce	5 mL
2 tsp	oil	10 mL
1	garlic clove, crushed	1
1	onion, chopped	1
1 cup	mushrooms, chopped	250 mL
2 tsp	cornstarch	10 mL
1 cup	skim milk	250 mL
1 Tbsp	tomato paste	15 mL
1	beef stock cube	1
2 cups	cooked noodles	500 mL

Cut beef into very thin strips. Place in a bowl with Worcestershire sauce and let stand for 10 minutes. Heat oil in frying pan and add garlic and beef. Stir fry for about 3 minutes. Add onion and mushrooms to pan and stir constantly for 2 minutes.

Blend cornstarch with a little of the milk. Add the cornstarch mixture, remaining milk, tomato paste, and beef stock cube to the beef mixture in the frying pan. Stir constantly over heat until mixture boils and thickens. Reduce heat and simmer uncovered for about 2 minutes. Serve over noodles.

Serves 3.

Nutritional analysis per serving:
356 calories   30 g protein   8 g fat   39 g carbohydrate   49 mg cholesterol

Lean cuts of beef include round, rump, and sirloin tip. To help make them tender, slice thinly against the grain. You may find it easier to slice the meat thinly when it is still partially frozen.

TAMALE PIE
Claudette Bertholet

This crustless meat pie is like a Tex-Mex version of shepherd's pie. Add other chopped vegetables along with the corn for more variety. Using less olives reduces the fat content even more.

1 cup	onion, chopped	250 mL
1 cup	green pepper, chopped	250 mL
3/4 lb	extra lean ground beef	340 g
2 cans	seasoned tomato sauce (8 oz/227 mL)	2 cans
1 can	whole kernel corn (12 oz/340 mL), drained	1 can
1 cup (or less)	chopped olives, drained	250 mL (or less)
1	garlic clove, minced	1
1 Tbsp	sugar	15 mL
1 tsp	salt	5 mL
2 – 3 tsp	chili powder	10 – 15 mL
	dash of pepper	
1/2 cup	part-skim cheese, shredded	125 mL

Corn Meal Topper

3/4 cup	yellow corn meal	200 mL
1/2 tsp	salt	2 mL
2 cups	cold water	500 mL
1 Tbsp	margarine	15 mL

Cook meat in a nonstick pan until lightly browned. Drain off any liquid. Add onion and green pepper and cook until just tender. Add tomato sauce, corn, olives, garlic, sugar, salt, chili powder, and pepper. Simmer 20-25 minutes until thick. Add cheese and stir until cheese is melted. Pour into casserole dish.

To make corn meal topper:

In a saucepan, stir cornmeal and salt into cold water. Cook and stir until mixture is thick. Add margarine and mix well. Spoon over hot meat mixture in 3 lengthwise strips.

Bake in 375°F oven for about 40 minutes.

Serves 6.

Nutritional analysis per serving:
374 calories   25 g protein   15 g fat   38 g carbohydrate   44 mg cholesterol

---

Most meat pies are high in fat because of the crust. If you have a **favourite** meat pie recipe, make individual "upside-down" pies by omitting **the** crust and using mashed potatoes as an "upper crust."

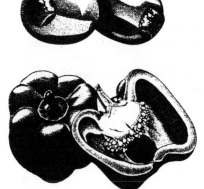

MARINATED FLANK STEAK

Ruth Grierson

Ruth has perfected this recipe from one her favourite cookbooks. It's easy to double or triple this recipe and freeze with the marinade for when unexpected company arrives. Delicious if served cold with a tossed salad.

2 lb	flank steak	900 g
1	garlic clove, chopped	1
1	onion, chopped	1
1 "knob"	fresh ginger, grated	1 "knob"
1/2 cup	soy sauce	125 mL
2 Tbsp	brown sugar	30 mL
2 Tbsp	lemon juice	30 mL
2 Tbsp	oil	30 mL
1/2 tsp	pepper	2 mL

In a Ziploc™ bag, blend all ingredients except steak. Place steak in marinade and refrigerate for at least 8 hours. Remove from marinade and barbecue or broil for 3 – 5 minutes on each side. To serve, slice thinly on the diagonal.

Serves 8.

Nutritional analysis per serving:
258 calories   24 g protein   15 g fat   5 g carbohydrate   60 mg cholesterol

Flank steak is a lean red meat that is often thought of as tough. Marinating the beef before cooking helps to tenderize it.

TWO TROPHY CHILI
Darrell Shaw

For a spicier chili, try adding a chopped chili pepper.

1 1/2 lb	**extra lean ground beef**	700 g
1	**large onion, chopped**	1
1	**green pepper, chopped**	1
3 cans	**kidney beans (14 oz/398 mL), drained**	3 cans
2 cans	**tomatoes (28 oz/796 mL)**	2 cans
1 can	**sliced mushrooms (10 oz/284 mL), drained**	1 can
2 tsp	**oregano**	10 mL
8 tsp	**chili powder**	40 mL
4 tsp	**cumin**	20 mL
1 Tbsp	**garlic powder**	15 mL

In a heavy saucepan brown ground beef for about 5 minutes. Pour off any fat. Add onions and peppers and cook over medium heat until onions are tender. Stir in beans, tomatoes, and mushrooms. Bring to a boil and simmer for one hour, stirring occasionally. Add spices and continue to simmer for 1 1/2 – 2 hours or until desired consistency is reached.

Serves 10.

Nutritional analysis per serving:
285 calories   22 g protein   9 g fat   30 g carbohydrate   42 mg cholesterol

Most tomato based sauces such as chili and spaghetti sauce taste even more delicious the second day as the flavours mingle.

POT ROAST ORIENTAL
William MacLeod

The combination of soy sauce and honey gives this dish the "flavour of the Orient." If you don't have a pressure cooker, use a covered roasting pan and bake at 325°F for about 2 1/2 hours. Serve with oven roasted vegetables and a green salad. Leftovers make delicious hot roast beef sandwiches.

1 tsp	garlic salt	5 mL
1/2 tsp	dry mustard	2 mL
1/4 tsp	pepper	1 mL
3 lb	lean beef pot roast	1.4 kg
3/4 cup	water	200 mL
1 1/2 tsp	oil	7 mL
2 Tbsp	soy sauce	30 mL
3 Tbsp	honey	45 mL
1 Tbsp	vinegar	15 mL
1 tsp	celery seed	5 mL
1/2 tsp	ginger	2 mL

Combine garlic salt, mustard, and pepper. Rub into roast. Heat pressure cooker and add oil. Brown roast. Mix together remaining ingredients and pour over the meat. Close cover securely. Place pressure regulator on vent pipe. Cook for 40 minutes. Let pressure drop off on its own before opening lid. Remove any fat and thicken gravy, if desired.

Serves 12.

Nutritional analysis per serving:
209 calories   33 g protein   7 g fat   2 g carbohydrate   72 mg cholesterol

Moist slow cooking methods such as braising help to tenderize less tender cuts of meat. Wine, water, stock or vegetable juices can be used as the liquid.

TENDER VEAL IN TOMATO SAUCE

William MacLeod

This is so tender, you can cut it with a fork. Serve this with steamed green vegetables and rice to soak up the tangy sauce.

6 oz	veal leg cutlets	200 g
2/3 cup	flour	175 mL
1 can	tomato soup (10 oz/284 mL)	1 can
5 oz	water	175 mL
1/2 tsp	oil	2 mL
	pepper to taste	

Cut veal into strips. Place flour and pepper into a plastic bag. Add the veal and shake until well coated with the flour mixture. Heat a nonstick frying pan on high heat. When hot add the oil. Sauté the veal until browned. Add the tomato soup, water and stir well. Sprinkle in the remaining flour, stirring continuously. Cover the frying pan and simmer for 1 hour, stirring often.

Serves 2.

Nutritional analysis per serving:
434 calories   35 g protein   8 g fat   53 g carbohydrate   111 mg cholesterol

STIR FRY PORK
Theresa Florkow

Pork tenderloin is lean yet tender. Try making this dish with chicken strips or thinly sliced beef instead of pork.

1 lb	boneless lean pork	454 g
1 Tbsp	margarine	15 mL
1 1/4 cups	chicken bouillon	300 mL
3 Tbsp	soy sauce	45 mL
1	onion, chopped	1
1 Tbsp	brown sugar	15 mL
1/4 tsp	salt	1 mL
1 tsp	fresh ginger, grated	5 mL
1/2 head	cabbage, shredded	1/2 head
2 stalks	celery, sliced	2 stalks
2 Tbsp	cornstarch	30 mL
2 Tbsp	cold water	30 mL

Slice pork thinly into 1 in/2.5 cm strips. In nonstick pan, melt margarine and brown pork strips. Add chicken bouillon, soy sauce and onion. Combine and stir in brown sugar, salt, and ginger. Cover and simmer for 30 minutes or until pork is tender. Add cabbage and celery and cook for a few minutes until vegetables are cooked. Blend cornstarch and cold water, and stir into cabbage mixture stirring until sauce is thickened. Serve over hot rice.

Serves 6.

Nutritional analysis per serving:
202 calories   25 g protein   5 g fat   15 g carbohydrate   70 mg cholesterol

Stir frying is a great way to emphasize flavour with very little added fat. A wok is the traditional pan used, but if you don't have one, any nonstick frying pan will do.

PORK WITH MUSTARD APPLE SAUCE
Marie Charpentier

The tanginess of the mustard and sweetness of the fruit makes a delicious flavour combination with pork. You can substitute grapes cut in halves for the apple.

12 oz	pork tenderloin	340 g
1/4 cup	flour	50 mL
1/4 tsp	salt	1 mL
	pepper to taste	
1 1/2 Tbsp	oil	22 mL
1	small onion, sliced	1
3/4 cup	chicken broth	200 mL
1/4 cup	dry white wine	50 mL
1 Tbsp	brown sugar	15 mL
1 Tbsp	Dijon mustard	15 mL
1 tsp	mustard seed	5 mL
1	apple, peeled and sliced	1

Cut pork into 1/2 in/2 cm slices. Mix together salt, pepper and flour. Dip pork pieces in flour mixture. Heat 1 Tbsp/15 mL of oil in nonstick pan and cook pork until done, about 5 minutes. Remove pork and set aside.

Add remaining 1/2 Tbsp/7 mL of oil to pan. Add onion and apple and sauté until tender. Add remaining ingredients. Bring to a boil and cook over medium heat, stirring occasionally until sauce is thickened. Add pork back to pan and heat until pork is warm.

Serves 3.

Nutritional analysis per serving:
311 calories   26 g protein   11 g fat   25 g carbohydrate   64 mg cholesterol

Pork was once considered a high fat meat. Pork tenderloin is actually very lean – a 3 oz/90 g serving has only 10 g fat.

SPAGHETTI WITH TURKEY MEATBALLS

John Peters

Prepare this sauce ahead of time and freeze it for a busy evening. The spices and herbs can be varied to suit your taste.

Part 1: Turkey Meatballs

1 lb	**ground turkey**	**454 g**
2 Tbsp	**skim milk**	**30 mL**
1	**egg**	**1**
1/4 cup	**dry bread crumbs**	**50 mL**
1/2 tsp	**oregano**	**2 mL**
1/2 tsp	**salt**	**2 mL**
	dash of pepper	

Combine all ingredients and mix well. Shape into about 24 – 1 in/2.5cm balls and place in a large baking pan. Bake at 375°F in the oven for about 20 minutes or until cooked.

Part 2: Spaghetti and Sauce

1 cup	**onion, chopped**	**250 mL**
1 cup	**green pepper, chopped**	**250 mL**
1/2 cup	**carrots, diced**	**125 mL**
1/2 cup	**celery, diced**	**125 mL**
2 cans	**tomatoes (16 oz/450 mL), chopped**	**2 cans**
1 can	**tomato paste (6 oz/175 mL)**	**1 can**
2 tsp	**basil or oregano**	**10 mL**
1/2 tsp	**sugar**	**2 mL**
1/2 tsp	**garlic powder**	**2 mL**
1/2 tsp	**salt**	**2 mL**
	turkey meatballs (from above)	
12 oz	**spaghetti, cooked and drained**	**340 g**

Cook onion, green pepper, carrots and celery in boiling water until tender. Drain. Add undrained tomatoes, tomato paste, and spices. Bring to a boil and reduce heat. Add meatballs. Cover and simmer for 30 minutes. Cook uncovered for a further 10 to 15 minutes if a thicker consistency is desired. Serve over hot cooked pasta.

Serves 6

Nutritional analysis per serving:
435 calories   25 g protein   8 g fat   67 g carbohydrate   92 mg cholesterol

Ground turkey is a nice alternative to beef, and is usually much lower in saturated fat. Check with the butcher to ensure that the "skin" has not been used.

CHICKEN FAJITAS
Shauna Ratner

Usually it's the guacamole, cheese and sour cream that break your fat budget with Mexican food. Load up on salsa, lettuce, tomatoes and nonfat sour cream or yogurt.

Part 1: Chicken

2	chicken breasts, skinned	2
1	lemon	1
1	lime	1
1 Tbsp	fresh cilantro, chopped	15 mL
1 tsp	olive oil	5 mL
1	yellow pepper, sliced into strips	1
1	red pepper, sliced into strips	1
1	green pepper, sliced into strips	1
1	onion, sliced into rounds	1
2 tsp	oil	10 mL
	red pepper flakes (optional)	

Squeeze the lemon and 1/2 the lime into a bowl. Add the cilantro red pepper flakes, and olive oil and mix well. Cut each chicken breast into strips and pour the marinade over the chicken. Refrigerate chicken covered for at least 1/2 hour to overnight.

In a large nonstick frying pan or a wok, heat the remaining oil. When oil is sizzling add the chicken strips and sauté until cooked. Remove chicken from pan and set aside. Add the peppers, onion and spices and sauté for 3-5 minutes (you may want to add some water) or until tender. Add the chicken pieces and heat through. Squeeze the remaining 1/2 lime over the mixture just before serving.

Part 2: Putting it all together

8	flour tortillas	8
1 cup	lettuce, shredded	250 mL
1	tomato, chopped	1
	nonfat sour cream or plain yogurt	
	salsa	

Warm the tortillas in the microwave or wrap in tin foil and heat at 350°F for 10 minutes.

To assemble the fajitas fill each flour tortilla with chicken vegetable mixture, lettuce and tomato. Top with nonfat sour cream or yogurt and salsa. Roll the tortilla. Serve immediately.

Serves 4.

Nutritional analysis per fajita:
212 calories   15 g protein   7 g fat   23 g carbohydrate   32 mg cholesterol

For a smoky flavour prepare the fajitas on the barbecue. Half the chicken breasts and grill until tender. Quarter the peppers and place sliced onions in a tin foil package and grill until the peppers are slightly charred. When done slice the chicken and peppers into strips and enjoy!

TURKEY IN MARSALA WINE SAUCE

Francois Bowden

Turkey is no longer just a festive dish; instead, it can be prepared in so many ways for any occasion. This particular dish with the flavour combination of chestnut and Marsala wine is an exciting change from the usual roast turkey.

1 (1 1/2 lb)	turkey breast, cut into 2 in/5 cm strips	1 (675 g)
1/2 cup	flour	125 mL
1 Tbsp	oil	15 mL
4	shallots, peeled and minced	4
1/2	onion, chopped	1/2
3/4 lb	mushrooms, sliced	400 g
2	carrots, cut into strips	2
1/2 cup	unsweetened chestnut puree	125 mL
1 cup	chicken stock	250 mL
2/3 cup	Marsala wine	150 mL
	paprika	
	salt and pepper to taste	

Combine flour with paprika, salt and pepper. Toss the turkey strips in this mixture until turkey is coated. Set aside.

Sauté shallots and onion in oil. Remove from pan and set aside.

Brown the turkey strips in the remaining oil. Remove and set aside.

In the same pan, combine chestnut puree, Marsala, and chicken stock. Mix until a thick sauce is formed. Add turkey, shallots, onions and other vegetables. Simmer until cooked, about one hour. Serve with steamed rice.

Serves 8.

Nutritional analysis per serving:
230 calories   28 g protein   5 g fat   13 g carbohydrate   71 mg cholesterol

Chestnut puree can be purchased in the canned food specialty section of your local supermarket. Chestnuts are the only nut that are virtually fat free.

HONEY BAKED CHICKEN
John Devereux

To enhance the flavour, the chicken can be marinated for several hours in the refrigerator prior to baking. Serve with basmati rice and stir fried vegetables for a quick and delightful meal.

4	chicken breast halves	4
2 Tbsp	Dijon mustard	30 mL
4 Tbsp	liquid honey	60 mL
1/2 tsp	curry powder	2 mL

Preheat oven to 325°F. Skin chicken breasts and place in oven dish just large enough to hold chicken pieces in a single layer. Stir remaining ingredients together and spread thickly over chicken pieces. Bake uncovered in centre of preheated oven for 45 minutes. Baste while baking and be careful not to let it burn.

Serves 4.

Nutritional analysis per serving:
266 calories   35 g protein   5 g fat   18 g carbohydrate   94 mg cholesterol

Chicken breasts although more expensive than other parts, are really quite reasonable in that there is very little waste. It's best to remove the skin before cooking, but if roasting or barbecuing where the fat drips down, skin can be removed before eating.

RUTH'S CHICKEN
Ruth Grierson

This recipe had rave reviews from the taste panel.

Part 1 – Chicken

4	**boneless skinless chicken breasts**	4
1/3 cup	flour	75 mL
2 Tbsp (or less)	oil	30 mL (or less)
2	onions, chopped	2
4	garlic cloves, minced	4
3	carrots, sliced	3
1 cup	pearl onions, peeled	250 mL
1 Tbsp	brown sugar	15 mL
1 tsp	ground cumin	5 mL
1 tsp	ginger	5 mL
3/4 tsp	curry powder	4 mL
3/4 tsp	salt	4 mL
1/2 tsp	cinnamon	2 mL
1/2 tsp	pepper	2 mL
1 can	tomatoes (19 oz/540 mL)	1 can
1/2 cup	chicken stock	125 mL
1	green pepper, chopped	1

Cut chicken breasts into chunks and coat with 1 Tbsp/15 mL of the flour. Cook chicken in saucepan with oil until browned. Remove chicken from pan and set aside. On medium heat, cook onions, garlic, carrots and pearl onions for 3 minutes. Stir in sugar, cumin, ginger, curry powder, salt, cinnamon, pepper and the rest of the flour. Stir and cook for 1 minute. Add tomatoes with juice and chicken stock, scraping up brown bits. Cook until boiling. Add green pepper and chicken to pan, cover and simmer for 1 hour. Transfer into shallow oven proof serving dish.

Part 2 – Topping

3	**sweet potatoes or yams**	**3**
1	**potato**	**1**
1/2 tsp	**salt**	**2 mL**
1/4 tsp	**pepper**	**1 mL**

Preheat oven to 375°F. Bake potato and sweet potatoes or yams until tender. Cool slightly, peel and cut into chunks. Process in food processor until smooth. Stir in salt and pepper. Spoon on top of chicken mixture in small mounds. Broil for 3 minutes until lightly browned.

Makes 4 servings.

Nutritional analysis per serving:
455 calories   32 g protein   11 g fat   57 g carbohydrate   71 mg cholesterol

SHREDDED CHICKEN WITH CUCUMBER

Angie Lim

This is very quick and easy to prepare. The mix of cucumbers and chicken together is a refreshing combination.

Part 1 – Chicken

1 lb	**boneless chicken (breasts or thigh)**	**454 g**
1	**green onion**	**1**
1	**slice ginger**	**1**

Place the chicken parts, ginger and green onion in a stockpot and cover with water. Bring to a boil, reduce heat and simmer until chicken is tender, about 1/2 hour. Remove the chicken skin and cut meat into strips. Set aside.

Part 2 – Dressing

1 1/2 tsp	**sugar**	**7 mL**
3 Tbsp	**soy sauce**	**45 mL**
1 tsp	**sesame oil**	**5 mL**
1 tsp	**salt**	**5 mL**
2	**cucumber, thinly sliced**	**2**

In a large bowl mix sugar, soy sauce, sesame oil and salt together. Add the chicken and cucumbers and mix well. Chill before serving.

Serves 4.

Nutritional analysis per serving:
224 calories   36 g protein   6 g fat   4 g carbohydrate   96 mg cholesterol

APRICOT CHICKEN DEVINE
Sylvia Loewen

Absolutely delicious! You can substitute 12 oz/340 g chicken or turkey breast for the chicken pieces.

1 tsp	oil	5 mL
2 – 3 lb	fryer chicken	1 – 1.5 kg
(skin removed, no necks, backs or wings)		
1/2 cup	flour	125 mL
1/2 cup	apricot jam	125 mL
1 Tbsp	Dijon mustard	15 mL
1/2 cup	skim milk yogurt	125 mL
2 Tbsp	slivered almonds, toasted	30 mL

Spread oil into ovenproof shallow baking dish. Cut chicken into pieces. Put flour in plastic bag and shake chicken in the bag until well coated. Place chicken on the pan in a single layer. Bake at 350°F for 25 minutes.

Combine jam, mustard and yogurt together and mix well. Spread mixture over the chicken and bake for an additional 25 – 30 minutes or until chicken is tender.

Bake almonds at 350°F for 5 minutes or until browned. Just before serving sprinkle chicken with toasted almonds.

Serves 4.

Nutritional analysis per serving:
393 calories   26 g protein   9 g fat   52 g carbohydrate   52 mg cholesterol

Freeze the chicken backs, necks and wings to have on hand when you want to make homemade chicken stock. Homemade stocks are much lower in sodium than store bought.

CHICKEN CHILI
Mary Parker

Chili is one of those versatile dishes that can be tasty made with beef, chicken, or even no meat. This particular version is a very quick one, especially if you have any leftover chicken or turkey. Using a can of beans in tomato sauce instead of the lemon juice will give the chili a rather mellow taste.

2	whole chicken breasts, skinless	2
1 Tbsp	olive oil	15 mL
3	onions, chopped	3
3	garlic cloves, minced	3
2 cans	kidney beans (16 oz/450 mL)	2 cans
2 cups	water	500 mL
1 can	tomatoes, chopped (16 oz/450 mL)	1 can
2 cans	tomato sauce (8 oz/227 mL)	2 cans
2 Tbsp	oregano	30 mL
2 tsp	chili powder	10 mL
1/4 cup	lemon juice	50 mL
	dash of cayenne pepper	
	dash of black pepper	

Simmer chicken breasts in water until tender. Remove from bones and cut into 1/4 in/1 cm pieces. Set aside.

Heat oil in a large pot over medium heat. Add onions and garlic and cook until softened. Add kidney beans, water, tomatoes, tomato sauce, oregano, chili powder, lemon juice and pepper and simmer uncovered for at least 1/2 hour (the longer you let the bean mixture simmer the more the flavours will meld together). Add chopped breasts and cook uncovered for 15 minutes over low heat or until chicken is heated through.

Serves 10.

Nutritional analysis per serving:
215 calories   21 g protein   4 g fat   25 g carbohydrate   38 mg cholesterol

CHICKEN IN TOMATO SAUCE
Ella Eisler

The whole family will like this. Use chicken breasts instead of legs if you prefer. Serve over broad noodles.

8	skinless chicken legs	8
2 Tbsp	oil	30 mL
1	onion, chopped	1
4	garlic cloves, minced	4
1 1/2 cups	celery, diced	375 mL
1 can	tomato paste (5 1/2 oz/156 mL)	1 can
11 oz	water	350 mL
2 Tbsp	vinegar	30 mL
2 Tbsp	lemon juice	30 mL
2 Tbsp	Worcestershire sauce	30 mL
2 Tbsp	brown sugar	30 mL
1 Tbsp	Dijon mustard	15 mL
	salt and pepper to taste	

In a medium size skillet heat oil. Add onion, garlic, celery, and sauté stirring often until onion is softened. Add remaining ingredients except chicken, and simmer for 15 minutes. Arrange chicken legs in roasting pan. Pour the sauce over the chicken and bake covered at 350°F for 1 hour.

Serves 5.

Nutritional analysis per serving:
155 calories   14 g protein   6 g fat   11 g carbohydrate   40 mg cholesterol

CHICKEN CACCIATORE
Marilyn Husdon

A simple low fat version of a popular dish. Add sautéed mushrooms and zucchini if you like.

6	chicken breasts, skinned	6
1	red onion, sliced	1
1 pkg	spaghetti sauce seasonings	1 pkg
1 can	tomatoes (19 oz/540 mL)	1 can

Brown the chicken breasts in a nonstick skillet. Place chicken in a shallow casserole dish and top each with an onion slice. Set aside.

Add the tomatoes and seasonings to the skillet and bring to a boil stirring constantly. Pour over the chicken and onions.

Cover the casserole and bake at 350°F for 1 hour or until chicken is tender.

Serves 6.

Nutritional analysis per serving:
221 calories   36 g protein   5 g fat   6 g carbohydrate   96 mg cholesterol

There are many varieties of low fat and sodium reduced tomato based spaghetti sauces now available. Use them as a base and add plenty of extra vegetables and fresh herbs.

CHICKEN CATALINA
Gail James

Salad dressing is a ready made marinade! It keeps the chicken moist and full of flavour.

4	boneless chicken breasts, skin removed	4
1 cup	calorie wise Catalina dressing™	250 mL
1/3 cup	white wine	75 mL
1/2 cup	green grapes, sliced lengthwise	125 mL

Cut the chicken into strips. Heat a wok over medium heat and brown the chicken in 1/3 cup/75 mL of the Catalina dressing™ until chicken is cooked through. Add the white wine, grapes and remainder of the salad dressing. Heat through.

Serves 6.

Nutritional analysis per serving:
230 calories   27 g protein   8 g fat   9 g carbohydrate   74 mg cholesterol

LEMON CHICKEN
John Harrop

Try this fresh tasting sauce with a firm fish fillet such as cod or red snapper. Brown the fish in the margarine or steam first before serving with the lemon sauce.

Part 1 – Chicken

4	**chicken breasts, halved and skin removed**	**4**
1 Tbsp	**margarine**	**15 mL**

Melt the margarine in a nonstick skillet and brown chicken until cooked. Cover and keep warm.

Part 2 – Sauce

1/2	**red pepper, finely chopped**	**1/2**
2 Tbsp	**brown sugar**	**30 mL**
1 Tbsp	**corn starch**	**15 mL**
2/3 cup	**water**	**175 mL**
3	**green onions, sliced diagonally**	**3**
1/4 cup	**lemon juice**	**50 mL**
1 tsp	**soy sauce**	**5 mL**
1	**chicken stock cube**	**1**
	salt and pepper to taste	

In a small sauce pan combine lemon juice, sugar, soy sauce, cornstarch, crumbled chicken stock cube, water, salt and pepper. Stir over low heat until sauce comes to a boil and thickens. Add red pepper and green onions. Mix well and pour over cooked chicken.

Serves 8.

Nutritional analysis per serving:
182 calories   27 g protein   5 g fat   5 g carbohydrate   74 mg cholesterol

Lemons are one of the most versatile flavourings for low fat cooking. Fresh lemons have the best flavour, but keep lemon from concentrate on hand for when your're in a pinch.

SOLE FILLETS IN CREAMY WINE SAUCE

Marie Charpentier

You can have dinner on the table in less than 20 minutes! The sauce tastes rich and creamy, and is a wonderful accompaniment to the fish. Serve with boiled potatoes and a green vegetable such as steamed broccoli.

1 Tbsp	**soft margarine**	**15 mL**
2 Tbsp	**green onions, chopped**	**30 mL**
1 lb	**sole fillets**	**454 g**
1 1/2 cups	**mushrooms, sliced**	**375 mL**
3/4 cup	**dry white wine**	**200 mL**
2 Tbsp	**flour**	**30 mL**
1/4 cup	**2% milk**	**50 mL**
1/2 tsp	**salt**	**2 mL**
1/2 tsp	**lemon juice**	**2 mL**
	dash of pepper	

Place margarine in 12 x 8 in/30 x 20 cm microwavable baking dish. Microwave at high power for 30 – 45 seconds or until margarine is melted. Spread melted margarine over the bottom of the baking dish and sprinkle with chopped onion. Arrange fillets over the onions, folding under the thin ends of the fillets. Top with mushrooms and add wine. Microwave at high for about 3 minutes or until fish flakes with a fork, turning dish once. Transfer fish and mushrooms to a microwavable platter. Cover and keep warm. Reserve liquid in baking dish.

In a 1 qt/1 L microwavable casserole dish, whisk together flour, milk, salt and pepper until smooth. Whisk in reserved liquid. Microwave at high power for 2 – 3 minutes or until thickened stirring every minute. Stir in lemon juice.

Drain any accumulated liquid off the fish. Pour sauce over fish and sprinkle with chopped parsley.

Makes 4 servings.

Nutritional analysis per serving:
218 calories   29 g protein   5 g fat   6 g carbohydrate   78 mg cholesterol

CRAB STUFFED SOLE
Eunice Melton

This is an elegant dish and quick to prepare. It's perfect for a special dinner. Serve it with a salad, rice pilaf and roasted asparagus.

1/4 cup	onion, chopped	50 mL
1/4 cup	green pepper, chopped	50 mL
1 can	crab meat (5 oz/140 g)	1 can
2 Tbsp	dry bread crumbs	30 mL
1/2 tsp	parsley flakes	2 mL
1/2 tsp	lemon pepper	2 mL
1/2 tsp	salt (optional)	2 mL
1 lb	sole fillets	454 g
1/2 cup	tomato sauce	125 mL
1/4 tsp	basil or oregano	1 mL
1/2 tsp	lemon juice	2 mL
3	lemon slices, halved	3

Combine onions and pepper together in a small bowl. Microwave on high power for 3 – 5 minutes or until tender, stirring every minute.

Rinse the crab meat and drain well. Stir crab, cooked onions and pepper, bread crumbs, parsley, salt and lemon pepper together to make the stuffing. Using half of the fish arrange a layer in microwavable safe pan. Spoon stuffing mixture evenly on the fish and cover with the remaining fillet. Set aside.

Mix tomato sauce, spices and lemon juice to make the sauce. Microwave on high power for 1 – 2 minutes, or until bubbly. Pour 1/4 cup/50 mL of the sauce over the fillets. Top with lemon slices. Cover with wax paper and microwave on medium for 11 – 15 minutes or until fish flakes. Rotate halfway through cooking. Serve with additional sauce.

Serves 6.

Nutritional analysis per serving:
136 calories   24 g protein   2 g fat   4 g carbohydrate   80 mg cholesterol

Until recently shellfish was considered on the "avoid" list for people with high cholesterol. New research has shown that only shrimp and squid are higher in cholesterol. Bivalves such as clams, oysters, scallops and mussels are low in both fat and cholesterol. Crabs and lobster contain moderate amounts of cholesterol.

SOLE FILLETS IN RED PEPPER SAUCE

Raquel Ciria

The roasted red peppers combined with dill give the fish a very refreshing flavour. Any fish fillet can be used instead of sole.

1	**red pepper, roasted**	1
1	**tomato**	1
1	**shallot**	1
1/3 cup	**water**	75 mL
1/2 tsp	**salt**	2 mL
1/2 tsp	**pepper**	2 mL
1 tsp	**dill**	5 mL
2/3 lb	**sole fillets, fresh**	300 g

Cut up the roasted red pepper, tomato and shallots into coarse chunks. Place pieces in a food processor. Add water, salt, pepper and dill and process until pureed. Put half of the sauce in the bottom of an oven proof dish. Arrange the sole fillets on top of the sauce in the dish. Spoon the remainder of the sauce on top of the fillets. Cover the dish and cook in the oven at 375°F for about 20 minutes or until fish is cooked.

Serves 3.

Nutritional analysis per serving:
139 calories   25 g protein   2 g fat   5 g carbohydrate   68 mg cholesterol

To roast red pepper: cook whole pepper in the oven at 375°F for about 45 minutes or until slightly darkened and easy to peel.

SALMON CANNELLONI WITH CREAMY LEMON SAUCE

Evelyn Priest

This is a much lower fat version of cannelloni in a cream sauce, but it still tastes as rich and satisfying. You could use cooked fresh salmon instead of canned if you like. Serve it with a mixed green salad – use a mixture of different greens such as Belgian endives, radicchio and watercress for an interesting touch.

Part 1 – Filling

12-14	cannelloni, cooked	12-14
2 cans	salmon, drained and flaked (7.5 oz/213 g)	2 cans
1/2 cup	skim yogurt	125 mL
2	green onions, chopped	2
1/2 tsp	grated lemon rind	2 mL
1/4 tsp	salt	1 mL

Combine the salmon, yogurt, onions, lemon rind and salt together and mix well. Spoon into cooked cannelloni. Set aside.

Part 2 – Sauce

3 Tbsp	margarine	45 mL
3 Tbsp	flour	45 mL
2 1/2 cups	skim milk	625 mL
1/4 tsp	thyme	1 mL
1/2 tsp	salt	2 mL
1 Tbsp	lemon juice	15 mL

Melt margarine in saucepan and stir in flour. Add milk, thyme and salt and cook stirring continuously until bubbling and smooth. Remove from heat and stir in lemon juice.

Pour a thin layer of the sauce in the bottom of a greased 13 x 9 in/33 x 23 cm pan or larger. Place prepared cannelloni in a single layer on top of the sauce. Cover with remaining sauce. Cover pan and bake at 350°F for 30 – 40 minutes.

Makes 12-14 cannelloni.

Nutritional analysis per cannelloni:
178 calories   11 g protein   6 g fat   19 g carbohydrate   10 mg cholesterol

SALMON WITH BLACK BEAN SAUCE

Ella Eisler

A true Westcoast dish!

4	**salmon steaks**	4
1 Tbsp	**fresh ginger, grated**	**15 mL**
1 Tbsp	**oil**	**15 mL**
2	**garlic cloves, crushed**	**2**
3	**green onions, chopped**	**3**
1 Tbsp	**rice or wine vinegar**	**15 mL**
2 Tbsp	**black bean sauce**	**30 mL**
1/2 cup	**chicken broth**	**125 mL**
1 Tbsp	**soy sauce**	**15 mL**
4 tsp	**corn starch**	**20 mL**

Preheat oven to 400°F. Sprinkle ginger on top of the salmon steaks and place in a casserole dish. Set aside.

Heat oil in a nonstick pan and sauté garlic and green onions until fragrant. Add the remaining ingredients and mix well. Bring to a boil while stirring, and cook one minute. Pour the sauce over the fish and bake for 15 minutes or until fish flakes easily.

Serves 4.

Nutritional analysis per serving:
222 calories   28 g protein   10 g fat   5 g carbohydrate   74 mg cholesterol

Even though salmon is a higher fat fish, it's great to eat. It's full of those omega-3 fatty acids which are so good for us.

SCALLOPS AND SNOW PEAS

Shirley Rose

Serve this fast very simple "stir fry" with steamed rice or noodles. If snow peas are not in season, try a combination of Chinese greens and red pepper.

1/2 lb	scallops	250 g
1/4 lb	snow peas	125 g
1/4 tsp	fresh ginger, minced	1 mL
2 tsp	cornstarch	10 mL
1 tsp	soy sauce	5 mL
1/4 cup	water	50 mL

Combine ginger, cornstarch, soy sauce and water and set aside.

Place scallops in a frying pan, add a little water, and cook over medium heat until scallops are white and opaque. Add snow peas and sauté for about 1 – 2 minutes, or until snow peas are tender, but still crisp. Add soy sauce mixture and cook while stirring until sauce is thickened.

Serves 2-3.

Nutritional analysis per serving:
146 calories   20 g protein   2 g fat   14 g carbohydrate   38 mg cholesterol

BAKED FISH WITH A SALSA DIFFERENCE

Ramona Josephson

Chunky style salsa will add bulk and body to any fish. The whole family will like this tangy dish.

4	**fish fillets** **(cod, halibut or snapper)**	4
2 tsp	**margarine, melted**	10 mL
2 tsp	**freshly squeezed lemon juice**	10 mL
1/2 tsp	**freshly ground black pepper**	2 mL
1	**green pepper, sliced**	1
10	**mushrooms, sliced**	10
1 cup	**chunky style salsa**	250 mL
	parmesan cheese, if desired	
	chopped parsley, if desired	

Preheat oven to 400°F. Layer baking dish with fish fillets. Cover with sliced peppers and mushrooms. Combine margarine, lemon juice and black pepper and pour over fish. Bake uncovered for 10 minutes. Pour salsa over fish and vegetables, and bake uncovered for an additional 5 minutes or until fish is done and salsa is heated. Top with a light sprinkle of parmesan cheese and chopped parsley, if desired.

Serves 4.

Nutritional analysis per serving:
150 calories   22 g protein   4 g fat   9 g carbohydrate   42 mg cholesterol

SAUCES AND MARINADES

Using just the right sauce or marinade can transform a simple dish into a mouthwatering taste treat. Commercial creamy sauces are usually quite high in fat, but now you can buy all kinds of tasty low fat non-creamy sauces to zest up your meals. Hoisin, plum, teriyaki, barbecue, salsa, sweet mustard sauces and their variations are just a few of the low fat sauces available today. Better yet, by making your own sauces, you can use ingredients to suit your particular preferences and needs.

Here are some suggestions:

• Red sauces with a tomato or vegetable base are usually lower in fat than creamy ones. Just be careful with the amount of oil used in the recipe.

• For a low fat "creamy" sauce, use skim milk, evaporated skim milk, yogurt, or nonfat sour cream. Thicken white sauces with instant blending flour (rather than making a roux) to give that rich consistency you want in a white sauce.

• For easy marinated vegetables, marinate cut up raw vegetables in low fat Italian dressing overnight.

• If you really prefer the taste of a particular favourite high fat dressing, dilute the dressing with a little vinegar and sugar to reduce the amount of fat in each serving.

• Instead of regular vinegar for sauces and dressings, try milder vinegars such as rice, apple cider or balsamic vinegar. You will then need less oil in your recipe to "mellow out" the acidity.

ORIENTAL-STYLE MARINADE
Hugh Green

Marinades give flavour to food and help to tenderize tough cuts of meat.

1	onion quartered	1
3	garlic cloves, sliced	3
1	piece fresh ginger (1 in/2.5 cm) cubed and peeled	1
1/2	jalapeno pepper, diced	1/2
1/4 cup	soy sauce	50 mL
1/4 cup	honey	50 mL
1 Tbsp	oil	15 mL

In food processor or blender, combine all ingredients and blend well. Coat the meat or chicken with mixture and allow to marinate overnight in refrigerator.

Makes 1 1/2 cups/375 mL.

Nutritional analysis per 1 Tbsp/15 mL:
22 calories   0 g protein   1 g fat   4 g carbohydrate   0 mg cholesterol

Marinate steak, chops, and chicken pieces for at least one hour before cooking. Marinate roasts and other large pieces of meat overnight.

LEMON MARINADES
Allan Ingram

In a medium size bowl or in a Ziploc™ bag pour marinade over chicken or fish. Cover or seal and let marinade in refrigerator for about one hour. Use extra sauce to baste while cooking.

1 – Lemon Dijon Marinade

1 Tbsp	**lemon juice**	**15 mL**
1 Tbsp	**white wine**	**15 mL**
1 Tbsp	**milk**	**15 mL**
1 Tbsp	**Dijon mustard**	**15 mL**
1/2 tsp	**basil**	**2 mL**

Mix ingredients until smooth. Makes 4 Tbsp/60 mL.

Nutritional analysis per 1 Tbsp/15 mL:
8 calories   0 g protein   0 g fat   1 g carbohydrate   0 mg cholesterol

2 – Lemon-Honey Marinade

1 Tbsp	**lemon juice**	**15 mL**
1 Tbsp	**honey**	**15 mL**
1 tsp	**soy sauce**	**5 mL**
	chopped garlic and ginger to taste	

Mix all ingredients until smooth. Makes 3 Tbsp/45 mL.

Nutritional analysis per 1 Tbsp/15 mL:
26 calories   0 g protein   0 g fat   7 g carbohydrate   0 mg cholesterol

YOGURT DRESSING
Robert Zaharia

This light salad dressing is good on a salad of mixed greens – use many different types of lettuces and add a variety of other fresh vegetables. It's also delicious as a dressing for potato salad.

1 cup	skim milk yogurt	250 mL
1	garlic clove	1
1 Tbsp	parsley, chopped	15 mL
2 Tbsp	lemon juice	30 mL
1/2 tsp	dill weed	2 mL
1/2 tsp	dry mustard	2 mL
1/2 tsp	sugar	2 mL
1/2 tsp	Worchestershire sauce	2 mL
1/2 tsp	pepper	2 mL
1/2 tsp	salt	2 mL
1/2	red or green pepper	1/2

Place all ingredients in a blender or food processor and puree. Pour into airtight container and store in refrigerator for up to ten days.

Makes 1 cup/250 mL.

Nutritional analysis per 1 Tbsp/15 mL:
10 calories   1 g protein   0 g fat   2 g carbohydrate   0 mg cholesterol

When substituting fresh herbs for dried, triple the amount. One tablespoon of fresh herbs is the equivalent of 1 teaspoon of dried herbs.

BUTTERMILK DRESSING
Ted Cohn

This Ranch style dressing has a light tangy taste and is a good substitute for commercial creamy dressings. Check the label on buttermilk to make sure that it is 2% milk fat or less.

1/4 cup	low fat buttermilk	50 mL
1/4 cup	plain skim yogurt	50 mL
2 Tbsp	apple cider vinegar	30 mL
1 Tbsp	lemon juice	15 mL
2 tsp	honey	10 mL
1 tsp	garlic, chopped	5 mL
2 Tbsp	green onions, chopped	30 mL
1/2 tsp	celery seed	2 mL

Combine all ingredients in a jar and shake until well blended. Refrigerate 15 minutes before serving.

Makes 3/4 cup/200 mL.

Nutritional analysis per 1 Tbsp/15 mL:
12 calories   1 g protein   0 g fat   2 g carbohydrate   0 mg cholesterol

LO-CAL DRESSING
Patricia Gillespie

This simple teriyaki-style dressing is very good on sliced tomatoes and cucumbers.

3 Tbsp	fresh lemon juice	45 mL
3 Tbsp	soy sauce	45 mL
1 Tbsp	sugar	15 mL

Whisk ingredients together in a small bowl. Pour over vegetables before serving.

Makes 6 Tbsp/90 mL.

Nutritional analysis per 1 Tbsp/15 mL:
14 calories   0 g protein   0 g fat   3 g carbohydrate   0 mg cholesterol

RUDY'S CAESAR SALAD DRESSING

This easily made dressing tastes great served over romaine lettuce pieces with homemade croutons.

1/3 cup	low fat plain yogurt	75 mL
1 tsp	olive oil	5 mL
2 Tbsp	red wine vinegar	30 mL
2 tsp	anchovy paste	10 mL
1	garlic clove, crushed	1
	salt and pepper to taste	

Combine all ingredients in a jar and shake until well blended. For best flavour, make ahead and store in the refrigerator.

Makes 1/2 cup/125 mL.

Nutritional analysis per 1 Tbsp/15 mL:
12 calories   1 g protein   1 g fat   1 g carbohydrate   1 mg cholesterol

To make homemade croutons: Lightly "butter" French bread slices with soft margarine. Cut bread into approximately 3/4 in/2 cm squares. Place them in a single layer on baking sheet. Sprinkle with garlic powder. Bake at 375°F until lightly browned.

SWEET AND SOUR SAUCE
Marg McQueen

Serve this sauce with poached, steamed or barbecued white fish.

2 Tbsp	sugar	30 mL
1 Tbsp	cornstarch	15 mL
1/2 tsp	chili powder	2 mL
2/3 cup	water	175 mL
3 Tbsp	ketchup	45 mL
1 Tbsp	cider vinegar	15 mL
1/4 cup	sweet pickle or relish	50 mL

In saucepan over medium heat, mix together sugar, cornstarch and chili powder. Stir in water, ketchup and vinegar and mix until smooth. Stirring continuously, bring mixture to a boil and cook until thickened. Cook for one minute longer. Remove from heat, and stir in sweet pickle or relish. Pour sauce over cooked fish before serving.

Makes about 1 cup/250 mL.

Nutritional analysis per 1 Tbsp/15 mL:
15 calories   0 g protein   0 g fat   4 g carbohydrate   0 mg cholesterol

SWEET MUSTARD SAUCE

This simple sauce is an adaptation of a recipe used at a local hospital years ago. It is delicious served with baked ham. Be sure to use very lean ham such as the precooked ready-to-eat type or turkey ham.

1/2 cup	vinegar	125 mL
1/2 cup	sugar	125 mL
1 Tbsp	mustard powder	15 mL
1	egg, slightly beaten	1

In a small saucepan, mix together sugar and mustard powder. Add vinegar and mix well. Whisk in beaten egg until mixture is smooth. Heat over low heat, stirring constantly until thickened.

Makes about 1 cup/250 mL.

Nutritional analysis per 1 Tbsp/15 mL:
32 calories   0 g protein   0 g fat   7 g carbohydrate   14 mg cholesterol

Mango Papaya Salsa
Shauna Ratner

This colourful salsa is delicious with grilled salmon. It's a great recipe for a dinner party or make half a recipe for a small gathering.

1	**papaya, peeled, seeds removed and diced**	1
1	**mango, diced**	1
1	**green pepper, diced**	1
1	**red pepper, diced**	1
1	**yellow pepper, diced**	1
1	**jalapeno pepper, diced**	1
1 Tbsp	**fresh lime juice**	15 mL
2 Tbsp	**balsamic vinegar**	30 mL
1 tsp	**extra virgin olive oil**	5 mL
	salt and pepper to taste	

Combine all ingredients together and let sit for at least 15 minutes to marinate. You can make this up to 8 hours in advance and refrigerate.

Makes 4 cups/1 L.

Nutritional analysis per 1/4 cup/50 mL:
31 calories   0 g protein   0 fat   7 g carbohydrate   0 mg cholesterol

FRESH TOMATO SALSA
Frances Johnson

Store bought salsa can be tasty, but none can beat the freshness and flavour of homemade tomato salsa. Serve with low fat tortilla chips or with fajitas.

1	**serrano or jalapeno pepper**	1
2	**garlic cloves**	2
1/2	**onion, cut into chunks**	1/2
4	**tomatoes, quartered**	4
1/4 cup	**fresh cilantro, chopped**	50 mL
2 Tbsp	**lemon juice**	30 mL
	salt to taste	

In food processor, grind pepper and garlic cloves until fine. Add onion and process until onion is coarsely chopped. Add tomatoes, cilantro, lemon juice and salt and process until tomatoes are chopped to desired consistency.

Makes about 2 cups/500 mL.

Nutritional analysis per 1/4 cup/50 mL:
14 calories   1 g protein   0 g fat   3 g carbohydrate   0 mg cholesterol

Tomatoes come in various shapes, sizes, textures and even colours. The added bonus is that they're all low in fat and calories. Use cherry tomatoes on vegetable trays with dips, roma tomatoes in marinated salads, thick slices of beefsteak tomatoes in vegetable sandwiches, and yellow tomatoes for added colour in a tossed salad.

BAKED GOODS

Everyone loves the taste and aroma of homemade goodies! Baked goods, such as muffins, cookies and loaves don't need to be rich and full of fat. It's possible to make flavour-packed treats without all that fat by making small adjustments to the recipe.

Try some of these tasty tips:

• Boost the fiber content with a mixture of whole wheat and white flour. You can substitute 1/2 the flour with a whole grain flour without changing the texture. If you like a heavier product, try using a little more whole grain flour.

• Use soft margarine or liquid oil instead of a hard fat. You really only need 1/4 cup of fat for 12 muffins or 1 loaf. Use yogurt or fruit purees to replace some of the fat.

• Use low fat yogurt, milk or buttermilk in place of higher fat dairy products.

• Substitute 2 egg whites for 1 whole egg, or use egg substitute.

• Try using fruit juices in place of water to enhance the flavour.

• Use cinnamon, nutmeg, cloves, orange or lemon zest or extracts to spice up loaves and muffins. These add flavour without the fat.

• Use chocolate chips, nuts and seeds in small amounts only. Even a small amount will provide lots of flavour. Try using raisins, chopped dates, dried cranberries or dried cherries.

RAISIN OATMEAL COOKIES
Evelyn Chaffey

Raisins and chopped dates add extra flavour to these cookies.

1 cup	whole wheat flour	250 mL
1 1/2 cups	rolled oats	375 mL
1/2 cup	skim milk	125 mL
1/2 tsp	salt	2 mL
1/4 cup	brown sugar, packed	50 mL
1/3 cup	oil	75 mL
1/2 tsp	baking soda	2 mL
2	egg whites	2
1 tsp	vanilla	5 mL
1/2 tsp	cinnamon	2 mL
1/2 tsp	nutmeg	2 mL
1 cup	raisins	250 mL
1/2 cup	dates, pitted and chopped	125 mL

In a mixing bowl, combine flour, rolled oats, salt, baking soda, cinnamon and nutmeg. Set aside. In another bowl cream oil and sugar. Beat in egg whites, milk and vanilla. Add mixed dry ingredients to liquid mixture and mix well. Stir in raisins and dates.

Drop batter by tablespoonful onto baking sheets sprayed with nonstick spray. Bake at 375°F for 12 – 15 minutes.

Makes 24 cookies.

Nutritional analysis per cookie:
120 calories   3 g protein   4 g fat   20 g carbohydrate   0 mg cholesterol

Low fat does not necessarily mean low calorie. Be careful not to "overdo" it when eating low fat sweet baked goods.

CHEWY OATBRAN MERINGUE COOKIES

Henry Shirley

Children will love these tasty treats – adults will too!!!

2	egg whites	2
1 tsp	vanilla	5 mL
1 cup	brown sugar	250 mL
1 cup	nuts, chopped	250 mL
3/4 cup	oat bran	200 mL
1/2 cup	raisins	125 mL
	pinch of salt	

Beat egg whites, salt and vanilla until foamy and soft peaks are formed. Gradually add brown sugar while beating. Fold in nuts, oatbran and raisins. Drop batter by spoonfuls onto baking sheets sprayed with nonstick spray. Bake at 350°F for 10 – 12 minutes.

Makes 36 cookies.

Nutritional analysis per cookie:
56 calories   1 g protein   2 g fat   9 g carbohydrate   0 mg cholesterol

Oat bran is the ground outer layer of the oat and is a good source of soluble fiber. Soluble fiber may help to lower blood cholesterol. Even if you are increasing your fiber intake, it's still more important to keep your diet low in fat.

BANANA BREAD

Try adding a handful of fresh blueberries in the summer, cranberries at Thanksgiving or a few chocolate chips for a special treat.

1 1/4 cup	**flour**	300 mL
1 tsp	**baking soda**	5 mL
1/2 tsp	**baking powder**	2 mL
1 cup	**sugar**	250 mL
1/4 cup	**oil**	50 mL
1/4 cup	**skim milk yogurt**	50 mL
1 tsp	**vanilla**	5 mL
1	**egg**	1
2	**egg whites**	2
2	**ripe bananas, mashed**	2

Combine dry ingredients and mix thoroughly. Set aside. In large mixing bowl combine oil, yogurt, egg, egg whites, vanilla and sugar. Beat well. Add bananas and mix. Add dry ingredients and mix well. Pour batter into 9 x 5 in/23 x 13 cm loaf pan sprayed with nonstick spray or line pan with tin foil. Bake at 350°F for 1 hour.

Makes 15 slices.

Nutritional analysis per serving:
144 calories   2 g protein   4 g fat   25 g carbohydrate   16 mg cholesterol

When you have extra ripe bananas and you don't feel like using them right away, put them in the freezer. Frozen bananas will keep in the freezer for months.

CHERRY LOAF
Anna Opper

This cake will add colour to any mixed dessert tray.

3/4 cup	white sugar	200 mL
1 Tbsp	melted margarine	15 mL
1	egg	1
1/2 cup + 2 Tbsp	1% milk	125 mL + 30 mL
2 cups	flour	500 mL
2 tsp	baking powder	10 mL
1 jar	maraschino cherries (medium size)	1 jar
1/4 cup	walnuts, chopped (optional)	50 mL

In medium size bowl beat sugar, melted margarine and egg together. Drain the cherries and reserve the juice. Cut cherries in half and shake with 1 Tbsp/15 mL of the flour. Set aside. Stir milk, flour, baking powder and cherry juice into the creamed mixture and mix well. Add cherries and nuts and mix gently.

Pour batter into 8 x 4 in/20 x 11 cm loaf pan sprayed with nonstick spray. Bake at 350°F for 45 minutes to 1 hour.

Makes 16 slices.

Nutritional analysis per slice:
125 calories   2 g protein   2 g fat   24 g carbohydrate   16 mg cholesterol

ZUCCHINI BREAD
Beverly Volk

This flavourful zucchini bread has no added fat! If you don't have any applesauce use yogurt instead. Five egg whites can be used in place of 3 whole eggs to make it cholesterol free too.

3	eggs	3
1 1/2 cups	white sugar	375 mL
1 cup	applesauce	250 mL
2 cups	flour	500 mL
1 tsp	salt	5 mL
1/4 tsp	baking powder	1 mL
2 tsp	baking soda	10 mL
1 tsp	cinnamon	5 mL
1 Tbsp	vanilla	15 mL
2 cups	zucchini, coarsely grated	500 mL
1 cup	raisins	250 mL
1/2 cup	walnuts, chopped	125 mL

In a medium size bowl combine flour, baking powder, baking soda, salt and cinnamon. Set aside. In a large bowl, beat eggs until foamy. Beat in applesauce, sugar and vanilla. Stir in zucchini. Add flour mixture and stir until combined. Stir in raisins and nuts. Divide batter between two 8 x 4 in/1.5 L loaf pans sprayed with nonstick spray. Bake at 350°F for 1 hour.

Each loaf makes 15 slices.

Nutritional analysis per slice:
104 Calories   2 g protein   2 g fat   21 g carbohydrate   23 mg cholesterol

Imagine adding a "squash" such as zucchini to a dessert! Vegetables like, zucchini, pumpkin and carrots are often added to baked goods to provide not only flavour but also moisture. Be careful of store bought vegetable or fruit breads – they are often full of oil and high fat.

PUMPKIN BREAD

Frances Johnson

This recipe was given to me by my friend Donata. She likes to make the recipe using walnuts and lots of raisins. If you don't have quite enough pumpkin, you can make up the difference using yogurt or applesauce.

3 cups	canned pumpkin	750 mL
1/2 cup	oil	125 mL
2 cups	sugar	500 mL
1 1/2 cups	oatmeal	375 mL
4 cups	flour	1 L
4 tsp	baking soda	20 mL
1 tsp	salt	5 mL
1 1/2 tsp	allspice	7 mL
1 1/2 tsp	cinnamon	7 mL
2 cups	raisins	500 mL
1/2 cup	chopped nuts (optional)	125 mL

In medium size bowl combine oatmeal, flour, baking soda, salt and spices together. Set aside. In large mixing bowl combine pumpkin, oil and sugar. Add dry ingredients and mix well. Stir in raisins and nuts. Divide batter into 2 loaf pans. Bake at 350°F for 1 hour or until done.

Makes 2 loaves each 15 slices.

Nutritional analysis per slice:
167 calories   3 g protein   5 g fat   28 g carbohydrate   0 mg cholesterol

CRANBERRY ORANGE LOAF
Frances Johnson

Cranberry and orange make a delightful combination in this tasty easy to prepare loaf. For a stronger orange flavour, omit the yogurt and use a total of 3/4 cup/175 mL orange juice.

2 cups	flour	500 mL
1 1/2 tsp	baking powder	7 mL
1/2 tsp	baking soda	2 mL
1/4 tsp	salt	1 mL
1 cup	sugar	250 mL
2 Tbsp	grated orange peel	30 mL
1 cup	cranberries, coarsely chopped	250 mL
1	egg beaten	1
1/4 cup	soft margarine, melted	50 mL
1/4 cup	orange juice	50 mL
1/2 cup	skim milk yogurt	125 mL

Combine dry ingredients with orange peel and mix thoroughly. Add cranberries and stir. Combine remaining ingredients and add to dry ingredients. Mix until just blended. Bake in 9 x 5 in/23 x 13 cm nonstick or foil-lined loaf pan at 350°F for 1 hour.

Makes 15 slices.

Nutritional analysis per slice:
148 calories   3 g protein   3 g fat   28 g carbohydrate   15 mg cholesterol

Cranberries add a rich colour and a zippy flavour to so many foods. Buy them fresh in the fall, or frozen anytime of the year. The fresh and frozen varieties can be used interchangeably in most recipes. Use dried cranberries in place of raisins or currants for a tangy change.

RAISIN OR BLUEBERRY MUFFINS
Helen Jones

Whole-wheat flour and bran make these muffins a good source of fiber.

1 Tbsp	**lemon juice**	**15 mL**
1 cup	**1% milk**	**250 mL**
1	**egg, beaten**	**1**
1/4 cup	**oil**	**50 mL**
1/4 cup	**molasses**	**50 mL**
1 cup	**natural bran**	**250 mL**
3/4 cup	**whole-wheat flour**	**200 mL**
3/4 cup	**all-purpose flour**	**200 mL**
1/3 cup	**brown sugar, packed**	**75 mL**
1 1/2 tsp	**lemon rind, grated**	**7 mL**
1 1/2 tsp	**baking powder**	**7 mL**
1/2 tsp	**baking soda**	**2 mL**
1/2 tsp	**salt**	**2 mL**
1 cup	**blueberries or raisins**	**250 mL**

In bowl, stir lemon juice into milk to "sour". Stir in egg, oil and molasses. Set aside. In another large bowl, combine bran, both flours, sugar, lemon rind, baking powder, baking soda and salt. Add milk mixture and blueberries or raisins. Spoon mixture into greased or paper lined muffin tins. Bake at 375°F for 20 – 25 minutes.

Makes 12 muffins.

Nutritional analysis per muffin:
132 calories   3 g protein   5 g fat   18 g carbohydrate   19 mg cholesterol

When blueberries are in season, buy extra for your freezer to enjoy the flavour of summer all year round. Freeze berries on a cookie tray in a single layer and pour into plastic bags.

BANANA APRICOT MUFFINS
Janet Van De Goede

These moist, high fiber muffins are delicious. Banana and apricot are a surprisingly good flavour combination.

1 1/2 cups	bran	375 mL
1 cup	whole wheat flour	250 mL
1 tsp	baking powder	5 mL
1 tsp	baking soda	5 mL
1/2 tsp	salt	2 mL
1/2 cup	dried apricots, chopped	125 mL
1/3 cup	oil	75 mL
1/3 cup	brown sugar	75 mL
1	egg, slightly beaten	1
3	ripe bananas, mashed	3
1 cup	low fat yogurt or buttermilk	250 mL

Combine bran, flour, baking powder, baking soda, salt and apricots together. Set aside. In large bowl combine oil, brown sugar, egg, bananas and yogurt. Mix well. Add dry ingredients to liquid mixture and mix until moistened.

Spoon mixture into muffin tins sprayed with nonstick spray or lined with paper muffin cups. Bake at 400°F for 30 minutes or until golden.

Makes 12 muffins.

Nutritional analysis per muffin:
190 calories   4 g protein   7 g fat   31 g carbohydrate   21 mg cholesterol   4g fiber

Since fresh apricots are available for such a short time, dried apricots are a handy alternative. These tasty dried fruits provide an even more intense flavour than the fresh. Keep in mind though that not only are they flavour packed, they are also calorie packed. Just 4 dried apricot halves is 40 calories!

RAISIN BRAN MUFFINS
Shelagh Smith

The molasses in these muffins provide moisture and an "old-fashioned" distinct flavour. Chopped dates or prunes can be used instead of raisins.

1 Tbsp	oil	15 mL
2 Tbsp	applesauce	30 mL
1/2 cup	brown sugar	125 mL
1/4 cup	molasses	50 mL
2	egg whites	2
1 cup	skim milk	250 mL
1 cup	flour	250 mL
1 1/2 tsp	baking powder	7 mL
1/2 tsp	baking soda	2 mL
1/2 tsp	salt	2 mL
1/2 cup	raisins	125 mL
1 1/2 cups	bran	375 mL

Beat egg whites until firm peaks form and set aside. Combine oil, applesauce, brown sugar and molasses and beat until smooth. Sift together flour, salt, baking soda and baking powder and add alternately with milk to molasses mixture. Add bran and raisins and stir until moistened. Fold in beaten egg whites. Spoon into greased or paper lined muffin tins. Bake at 400°F for 15 – 20 minutes.

Makes 12 large muffins.

Nutritional analysis per muffin:
147 Calories   4 g protein   1 g fat   33 g carbohydrate   0 mg cholesterol   3 g fiber

Store bought monster muffins are often just cupcakes in disguise! By making muffins at home, you can create any number of varieties of moist, yet low fat muffins. Ingredients such as yogurt, pureed fruit, buttermilk, molasses and dried fruit help to maintain the moisture and texture without the fat.

6 WEEK BRAN MUFFINS
Loretta Byrnes

Imagine having muffin batter whenever you need it! Not only is the batter easy to make, the muffins are delicious and moist. Use any combination of fruit to suit your taste.

2 cups	boiling water	500 mL
1 cup	applesauce	250 mL
4	egg whites, beaten	4
5 cups	flour (mixture of 3 cups/750 mL whole wheat, 1 cup/250 mL oat bran, 1 cup/250 mL white flour is good)	1.25 L
5 tsp	baking soda	25 mL
4 cups	1.5% m.f. buttermilk	1 L
4 cups	branflakes	1 L
2 cups	Bran Buds™ or All Bran™	500 mL
1/2 cup	molasses	125 mL
1 cup or more	raisins	250 mL or more
1 cup	dates (optional)	250 mL
2	bananas (optional)	2
1 cup	prunes (optional)	250 mL
1 cup	any fruit (optional)	250 mL

Add soda to boiling water. Set aside and let cool. Combine applesauce and beaten egg whites. Blend well. Stir in buttermilk and molasses. Add soda water mixture and mix well. Combine remaining dry ingredients and fruit. Add dry ingredients to liquid ingredients and mix only until blended. Do not overmix. Place batter as needed in greased or muffin tins sprayed with nonstick spray. Bake at 350°F for 20 – 25 minutes or until toothpick inserted in center comes out clean. The batter can be kept in the refrigerator for up to 6 weeks.

Makes 4 to 5 dozen.

Nutritional analysis per muffin:
114 Calories   3 g protein   1 g fat   25 g carbohydrate   2 mg cholesterol

It is recommended that we eat 25 – 30g of fiber per day. Best sources of fiber are fresh fruits and vegetables, and whole grains. Choose *whole fruits and vegetables* rather than juices, and *whole grains* instead of refined products whenever you can.

OAT BRAN MUFFINS
Shirley Rose

These easy to make moist muffins are delicious. Try making them with chopped dates or dried cranberries instead of raisins.

1 cup	whole wheat flour	250 mL
1/2 cup	sugar	125 mL
1 1/2 cups	oat bran	375 mL
2 tsp	baking powder	10 mL
1 tsp	baking soda	5 mL
1/2 tsp	cinnamon	2 mL
1	egg, beaten	1
1 cup	1.5% m.f. buttermilk	250 mL
1/4 cup	oil	50 mLs
1/4 tsp	vanilla	1 mL
1/2 cup	raisins	125 mL

In a bowl, combine flour, sugar, oat bran, baking powder, baking soda and cinnamon. Mix well. Add egg, buttermilk, oil, vanilla, and raisins. Stir until just blended. Spoon mixture into paper lined or muffin tins sprayed with nonstick spray. Bake at 400°F for 20 minutes.

Makes 12 muffins.

Nutritional analysis per muffin:
175 Calories   5 g protein   6 g fat   31 g carbohydrate   21 mg cholesterol   2 g fiber

White sugar, brown sugar, honey, corn syrup, and maple syrup are practically identical when it comes to our bodies. All of these products are "sugar" and give us energy, but do not give us many vitamins.

SCONES
Marg McQueen

These scones are yummy as they are, or they can make a great base for strawberry shortcake.

1 3/4 cups	**flour**	**450 mL**
1 Tbsp	**baking powder**	**15 mL**
2 Tbsp	**sugar**	**30 mL**
1/4 tsp	**salt**	**1 mL**
1/4 cup	**oil**	**50 mL**
2/3 cup	**skim milk**	**175 mL**
1/2 cup	**raisins or currants (optional)**	**125 mL**

Combine flour, baking powder, salt and sugar in a medium size mixing bowl. Mix thoroughly. Add the raisins. Make a well in the flour mixture. Add the milk and oil all at once, and stir until moistened. Line a baking sheet with parchment paper or spray with nonstick spray. Pat down on baking sheet until 3/4 in/2 cm thick circle. With knife, score dough into 9 wedges. Bake at 450°F for 8 – 10 minutes.

Makes 9 pieces.

Nutritional analysis per wedge:
189 Calories   3 g protein   6 g fat   30 g carbohydrate   0 mg cholesterol

Store-bought scones are often high in fat. Better choices are bagels (they're really like low fat doughnuts!), English muffins, soft pretzels, and crumpets.

SWEET FINALES

Fresh fruit is always the best choice for dessert, but sometimes we all want that "extra something." Although traditional desserts can be high in fat and sugar, there are many delicious choices which don't have to break your fat budget. You can also adjust your favourite recipes to lower the fat content without taking away the inviting look or taste of a special dessert.

Try some of the following ideas:

• Substitute 2 egg whites for 1 whole egg. You may want to use a mixture of whole eggs plus egg whites. If you don't like discarding the yolks, you can buy just egg whites in the dairy section of most grocery stores.

• Cut the fat right down. Use yogurt or fruit purees such as applesauce, mashed bananas or prune paste to replace some of the fat.

• Replace higher fat dairy products with skim milk products such as skim milk, low fat yogurt, light or fat free sour cream, and light cream cheese.

• Use frozen yogurt, sherbet, fruit ice or ice milk as a topping instead of ice cream.

• Use angel food cake as a base for shortcake type desserts – top with sliced fresh fruit and a dab of Light Cool Whip.™

• Use nuts and seeds in small amounts only. Even a tiny amount will provide the nutty flavour you want.

• Make sure to balance your fat budget - if you decide to have a richer dessert, then make sure the rest of the meal is lower in fat! Remember that half a portion contains half the fat.

KEY LIME SNOW
Ruth Grierson

An absolutely refreshing dessert that bursts with flavour! Any citrus fruit can be used instead of lime.

2 envelopes	unflavoured gelatin	2 envelopes
1/2 cup	cold water	125 mL
3/4 cup	sugar	200 mL
1 1/2 cups	boiling water	375 mL
1/2 tsp	grated lime peel	2 mL
1/2 cup	lime juice	125 mL
4	egg whites	4

Sprinkle unflavoured gelatin over cold water in a large bowl and let stand five minutes. Stir in sugar until blended. Add boiling water and stir until gelatin is completely dissolved, about 3 minutes. Add grated lime peel and lime juice. Chill until slightly thickened, about 15 minutes.

Beat egg whites until stiff. While beating, gradually add gelatin mixture until soft peaks form. Spoon into 8 individual dessert cups or 1 large serving bowl. Chill for 2 hours. Garnish with twisted lime peel.

Serves 8.

Nutritional analysis per serving:
64 calories   3 g protein   0 g fat   14 g carbohydrate   0 mg cholesterol

We tempt our eyes before our palate. A garnish can make all the difference in a first impression. Use mint leaves, edible flowers, or whole berries to garnish some desserts.

BLUEBERRY FLAN
Sylvia Loewen

A light alternative to cheesecake. Try using lemon rind instead of orange rind for a different flavour.

Part 1 – Crust

1 1/2 cups	flour	375 mL
1/2 cup	sugar	125 mL
1 1/2 tsp	baking powder	7 mL
1/3 cup	soft margarine	75 mL
2	egg whites	2
1 tsp	vanilla	5 mL

Part 2 – Filling

3 cups	blueberries	750 mL
2 Tbsp	flour	30 mL
2 cups	plain skim milk yogurt	500 mL
2	egg whites	2
1/2 cup	sugar	125 mL
2 tsp	grated orange rind	10 mL
1 tsp	vanilla	5 mL

In mixing bowl, combine flour, sugar, baking powder, margarine, egg whites and vanilla. Mix well. Press into the bottom of a 10 in/25 cm spring form or flan pan. Spread blueberries on top of the base.

In mixing bowl, add flour to yogurt and mix. Add egg whites, sugar, rind, and vanilla. Mix until smooth. Spread over blueberries in pan.

Bake at 350°F for 1 hour or until golden. Cool and refrigerate.

Serves 12.

Nutritional analysis per serving:
217 calories   5 g protein   5 g fat   38 g carbohydrate   1 mg cholesterol

CHOCOLATE MOCHA CAKE
Mary Parker

It's hard to believe you can make a chocolate cake without any added fat, but the result is surprisingly tasty.

1 1/2 cups	flour	375 mL
1 1/3 cups	sugar	325 mL
1/2 cup	cocoa	125 mL
1 1/4 tsp	baking soda	6 mL
3/4 tsp	baking powder	4 mL
1/2 tsp	salt	2 mL
3	egg whites	3
3/4 cup	coffee, cooled	200 mL
1/2 cup	skim milk	125 mL
1/3 cup	corn syrup	75 mL

Frosting

2/3 cup	corn syrup	175 mL
1	egg white	1
3/4 tsp	instant coffee powder	4 mL

In a large bowl, combine flour, sugar, cocoa, baking soda, baking powder, and salt. Set aside. In a small bowl, whisk remaining ingredients together to blend well. Add liquids to dry ingredients, whisking until smooth. Pour into 9 in/23 cm square pan sprayed with nonstick spray. Bake at 350°F for 35 – 40 minutes or until done. Cool completely and frost, if desired.

Frosting

Bring syrup to a boil. In a bowl beat egg white until soft peaks are formed. Add coffee powder and very gradually beat in hot syrup. Continue beating until stiff and shiny, about 3 minutes. Spread over cooled cake.

Makes 16 servings.

Nutritional analysis per serving:
Cake only: 145 calories   4 g protein   1 g fat   30 g carbohydrate   0 mg cholesterol

With frosting: 185 calories   4 g protein   1 g fat   40 g carbohydrate 0 mg cholesterol

PAVLOVA
Jiri Frohlich

Pavlova is an elegant light dessert made with a meringue base covered with fresh fruit and whipped topping.

4	**egg whites**	4
1 cup	**sugar**	250 mL
1/2 tsp	**vanilla**	2 mL
1 Tbsp	**vinegar**	15 mL
2 cups	**Light Cool Whip™**	500 mL
1/4 cup	**toasted sliced almonds**	50 mL

fresh fruit such as sliced strawberries, papaya, kiwi, or blueberries

In a glass bowl, whip egg whites until soft peaks are formed. Beat in sugar, vanilla, and vinegar. Whip until stiff peaks are formed. Line a baking sheet with parchment or brown paper. Spread meringue mixture onto paper in a flat round shape. Bake at 275°F for 1 hour. Turn oven off and leave meringue in oven until oven is cool (several hours). Just before serving, top with whipped topping, fresh fruit and toasted almonds.

Nutritional analysis per serving:
229 calories   4 g protein   8 g fat   43 g carbohydrate   0 mg cholesterol

Regular whipping cream has a whopping 88 grams of fat per cup! That's why using a light whipped topping or frozen yogurt makes a lot of sense.

Light Lemon Cheesecake
Rose Smirl Vernon

This is a wonderful dinner party dessert. No one will ever guess that it is low in fat! You could make it with orange juice and orange peel instead of lemon.

1 1/2 cups	2% cottage cheese	375 mL
2 tsp	grated lemon peel	10 mL
1 packet	unflavoured gelatin	1 packet
1/4 cup	fresh lemon juice	50 mL
3 Tbsp	sugar	45 mL
3	eggs, separated	3
1/2 cup	2% milk	125 mL
1 tsp	vanilla	5 mL
1/4 tsp	cream of tartar	1 mL

Sprinkle gelatin over lemon juice to soften. Set aside for 5 minutes. Beat cottage cheese or press through a sieve until very smooth. Stir in lemon peel. Whisk together egg yolks and milk in top of double boiler. Cook over simmering water, stirring until mixture thickens slightly and coats a metal spoon. Remove from heat. Add gelatin mixture and stir until dissolved. Add sugar, vanilla and cottage cheese. Chill, stirring occasionally until mixture mounds when dropped from a spoon.

Beat egg whites with cream of tartar until stiff peaks form. Fold into gelatin mixture. Pour over graham wafer crust (see below). Sprinkle any remaining graham crumbs on top. Chill for 4 hours or until firm. Serve with berry sauce.

Graham wafer crust

3/4 cup	graham wafer crumbs	200 mL
3 Tbsp	margarine, melted	45 mL
1/4 tsp	cinnamon	1 mL
1/4 tsp	nutmeg	1 mL

Combine all ingredients. Press into 9 in/23 cm pie plate or spring form pan. Save 2 Tbsp/30 mL of the crumb mixture for the top of the cheesecake. Bake at 350°F for 10 minutes. Let cool.

Berry Sauce

1 cup	frozen unsweetened raspberries or strawberries	250 mL
4 Tbsp	sugar	60 mL
1 Tbsp	fresh lemon juice	15 mL

Combine all ingredients and mix well. A sugar substitute can be used instead of sugar if desired. Makes about 3/4 cup/200 mL.

Makes 8 servings.

Nutritional analysis per serving:
197 calories   11 g protein   9 g fat   19 g carbohydrate   87 mg cholesterol

LEMON CHIFFON CHEESECAKE
Hannelore Vannetta

This no-bake cheesecake is light and fluffy. Serve it with a pureed fruit sauce.

Part 1 – Crust

1/4 cup	soft margarine	50 mL
1 1/4 cups	graham wafer crumbs	300 mL
2 Tbsp	sugar	30 mL

Part 2 – Filling

2 packages	unflavoured gelatin	2 packages
1/2 cup	cold water	125 mL
1 cup	sugar	250 mL
1 tsp	salt	5 mL
2	egg yolks	2
1/2 cup	2% milk	125 mL
2 cups	1% cottage cheese, pureed in blender	500 mL
	grated rind and juice of one lemon	
1 tsp	vanilla	5 mL
2	egg whites	2
1 cup	Light Cool Whip™	250 mL

For crust: Melt margarine in saucepan or microwave. Add crumbs and sugar, and mix. Press into bottom and sides of an ungreased 9 in/22 cm springform pan. Bake at 350°F for 10 minutes. Let cool.

For filling: Sprinkle gelatin over cold water in top of double boiler and let stand 5 – 10 minutes to soften. Place over boiling water. Add yolks one at a time beating well with spoon after each addition. Stir in milk, sugar, and salt. Heat and stir until gelatin and sugar are dissolved. Chill until syrupy consistency. Fold in cottage cheese, lemon rind, lemon juice, and vanilla. Whip egg whites until stiff and fold into gelatin mixture. Then fold in whipped topping. Pour over crumbs. Chill until set.

Serves 12.

Nutritional analysis per serving:
217 calories   8 g protein   8 g fat   31 g carbohydrate   38 mg cholesterol

RAISIN CAKE

We're not quite sure who provided this recipe, but it's a deliciously moist cholesterol-free spice cake.

2 cups	**raisins**	**500 mL**
1 cup	**water**	**250 mL**
1 cup	**brown sugar, packed**	**250 mL**
1/3 cup	**soft margarine**	**75 mL**
1 tsp	**cinnamon**	**5 mL**
1/4 tsp	**cloves**	**1 mL**
1/4 tsp	**nutmeg**	**1 mL**
1 tsp	**baking soda**	**5 mL**
1 tsp	**water**	**5 mL**
2 cups	**flour**	**500 mL**
1 tsp	**baking powder**	**5 mL**
1/4 tsp	**salt**	**1 mL**

Combine first seven ingredients in saucepan. Heat until boiling, stirring occasionally. Boil for 3 minutes. Remove from heat. Stir baking soda into 1 tsp/5 mL water. Add to saucepan. Mix together flour, baking powder and salt. Add to mixture and mix until well blended. Pour into 9 x 5 in/22 x 12 cm loaf pan sprayed with nonstick cooking spray. Bake at 350°F for 40 minutes or until toothpick inserted in middle comes out clean.

Serves 12.

Nutritional analysis per serving:
195 calories   2 g protein   5 g fat   37 g carbohydrate   0 mg cholesterol

For festive occasions, include some low fat cakes and squares on the dessert tray to go along with the traditional treats.

KWIK KAKE
Margaret McDonald

This recipe is easy to double and freeze for when unexpected company arrives. Try adding a handful of raisins or currants, or use rolled oats instead of all bran for variety.

2	**tea bags**	**2**
1 cup	**water**	**250 mL**
1/2 cup	**all bran or bran buds**	**125 mL**
1/4 cup	**oil**	**50 mL**
1 Tbsp	**white vinegar**	**15 mL**
1 tsp	**vanilla**	**5 mL**
1 1/4 cups	**flour**	**300 mL**
1 cup	**sugar**	**250 mL**
1/4 cup	**cocoa**	**50 mL**
1 tsp	**baking soda**	**5 mL**
1/2 tsp	**salt**	**2 mL**
1/2 tsp	**cinnamon**	**2 mL**

Bring water to a boil and pour over tea bags. Let steep for 5 minutes. Remove tea bags. Add bran to tea and let sit. When most of the moisture is absorbed stir in oil and vanilla. Mix together remaining ingredients and add to bran mixture. Mix well.

Spray 8 in/20 cm square pan with nonstick spray. Pour batter into pan. Bake at 350°F for 35 minutes or until toothpick inserted in the middle comes out clean. Cool and dust with icing sugar.

Serves 16.

Nutritional analysis per serving:
124 calories   2 g protein   4 g fat   21 g carbohydrate   0 mg cholesterol

Cocoa powder has no fat and is a good alternative to chocolate.

LEMON CHIFFON CAKE
Mary Sugiyama

Although there are several steps to this recipe, preparation is really quite simple. It produces a flavourful yet light, refreshing dessert. For a lighter cake, omit the glaze and finish the cake with a light dusting of icing sugar.

1 1/2 cups	flour	375 mL
1 cup	sugar	250 mL
2 tsp	baking powder	10 mL
1/4 tsp	salt	1 mL
3	large egg whites	3
2 Tbsp	icing sugar	30 mL
1/4 cup	oil	50 mL
1/4 cup	water	50 mL
	grated rind of 2 lemons	
1/2 cup	lemon juice	125 mL

Mix together flour, sugar, baking powder and salt. Make well in the centre. Set aside. In another bowl, combine egg whites and icing sugar and beat until stiff. Set aside. In a small mixing bowl, mix together oil, water, lemon juice and lemon rind. Pour mixture into dry ingredients and stir well. Fold beaten egg whites into batter. Bake in nonstick bundt or tube pan sprayed with nonstick spray at 350°F for 35 minutes or until done.

Glaze:

1 1/2 cups	icing sugar (or less)	375 mL
2 tsp	lemon rind, grated	10 mL
2 Tbsp	lemon juice	30 mL

Mix together sugar, lemon rind and lemon juice. Glaze when cake is cooled. Makes 16 slices.

Nutritional analysis per slice:
197 calories   2 g protein   4 g fat   41 g carbohydrate   0 mg cholesterol

APPLE CAKE
Eva Benkovich

Instead of making apple pie which is usually high in fat, make this scrumptious apple cake to use up all those apples in the fall.

2 cups	apples, peeled and grated	500 mL
1/2 cup	sugar	125 mL
1 1/4 cup	flour	300 mL
1	egg white, beaten	1
1/4 cup	oil	50 mL
1/4 cup	walnuts, chopped	50 mL
1 tsp	cinnamon	5 mL
1 tsp	baking soda	5 mL
1/2 tsp	salt (optional)	2 mL

In mixing bowl, combine flour, sugar, cinnamon, baking soda, walnuts and salt. Mix well. Add apples, egg white and oil. Stir until combined. Batter will be very thick.

Spray 8 x 10 in/20 x 25 cm baking pan or 10 in/25 cm round springform pan with nonstick spray and pour batter into pan. Bake at 350°F for 30 – 35 minutes, or until done.

Serves 12.

Nutritional analysis per serving:
141 calories   2 g protein   5 g fat   23 g carbohydrate   0 mg cholesterol

It's so easy to make homemade applesauce – peel, core and slice apples and cover with water (about 2 Tbsp water per apple). Add sugar to taste if you like. Simmer until apples are soft. Remove from heat and mash to desired texture – add vanilla for a mellow delicious flavour.

CARROT CAKE
Madeline Foslien

This "yummy" carrot cake is lightened by using low fat yogurt and egg substitute. The yogurt topping is a wonderful alternative to cream cheese icing.

2 cups	**flour**	**500 mL**
1 1/2 cups	**sugar**	**375 mL**
2 tsp	**baking soda**	**10 mL**
2 tsp	**cinnamon**	**10 mL**
1 tsp	**baking powder**	**5 mL**
1 can	**crushed pineapple, (8 oz/238 mL)**	**1 can**
1 cup	**plain skim milk yogurt**	**250 mL**
1/4 cup	**egg substitute**	**50 mL**
1/4 cup	**oil**	**50 mL**
3 cups	**shredded carrots**	**750 mL**
3/4 cup	**raisins**	**175 mL**

Spray 13 x 9 in/33 x 23 cm baking pan with nonstick spray. In a large bowl combine flour, sugar, baking soda , baking powder and cinnamon. Stir in pineapple, yogurt, egg substitute and oil. Add carrots and raisins and mix until blended.

Pour into pan. Bake at 325°F for 40 – 45 minutes.

Yogurt Topping

1 1/2 cups	**plain skim milk yogurt (should not contain starch, gelatin or gums)**	**375 mL**
3 Tbsp	**brown sugar**	**45 mL**
1 tsp	**vanilla**	**5 mL**

Line a sieve with a cheesecloth and set over bowl. Add the yogurt and let drip for 2 hours. Add brown sugar and vanilla and refrigerate. Ice cooled cake with topping or spoon over pieces before serving.

Serves 18.

Nutritional analysis per serving:
213 calories   4 g protein   4 g fat   42 g carbohydrate   1 mg cholesterol

CREPES
Frances Johnson

Crepes are a great alternative to pies for using fruits in season such as strawberries, blueberries, or peaches. Crepes can be frozen for later use – place waxed paper between them, put in an airtight container and freeze. When you are ready to serve the crepes, thaw and warm in the microwave oven and serve with your favourite filling or topping.

2	eggs	2
2	egg whites (or use 3/4 cup/200 mL egg substitute instead of eggs and egg whites)	2
1 cup	skim milk	250 mL
1/2 cup	water	125 mL
2 Tbsp	margarine, melted	30 mL
1 cup	flour	250 mL
1 Tbsp	sugar	15 mL
1/4 tsp or less	salt	1 mL or less

In mixing bowl, beat eggs, egg whites, milk, water and margarine. Blend in dry ingredients until smooth. Cover and refrigerate for at least 1 hour. Stir before cooking.

Grease non stick 7 in/18 cm skillet with 1 tsp/5 mL margarine. Heat over medium high heat. Pour batter (about 2-3 Tbsp/30-45 mL) into pan, tilting pan so batter coats the bottom. Cook about 1 minute or until lightly browned. Flip and cook the other side for 30 seconds or until lightly browned. Use immediately, or cover tightly and store in refrigerator for up to 3 days.

Makes 16 – 7 in/18 cm crepes.

Nutritional analysis per crepe (crepe only):
62 calories   3 g protein   2 g fat   8 g carbohydrate   29 mg cholesterol

For fillings or toppings for crepes, choose fruit preserves, canned fruit pie filling, or sliced fresh strawberries sweetened with a little honey or sugar. Combining thickened stewed fruit with some fresh sliced fruit gives a very refreshing touch. Top the crepe with a sprinkle of icing sugar, light whip topping or frozen yogurt.

MUDBALLS
Allan Ingram

No one will believe that these are low fat! For a fancier treat roll them in icing sugar .

2 cups	sugar	500 mL
1 cup	1% milk	250 mL
1/4 cup	soft margarine	50 mL
3 1/2 cups	rolled oats	875 mL
1 tsp	vanilla	5 mL
6 Tbsp	cocoa powder	90 mL
	pinch salt	

Mix together sugar, milk and margarine in a medium size pot. Bring to a boil and let boil for 10 minutes. In another bowl mix rolled oats, vanilla, cocoa powder and salt. Pour the hot mixture into the oat mixture and stir well. Form into 1 in/2.5 cm balls.

Makes 60 mudballs.

Nutritional analysis per ball:
53 calories   1 g protein   1 g fat   10 g carbohydrate   0 mg cholesterol

By using cereals in making desserts you get the added benefit of fiber, B vitamins and iron. Rice Krispie Squares, Puffed Wheat Squares and fruit crisps are just a few tasty examples.

APPLE MERINGUE PUDDING

Maria Ragone

This crustless pie is great to make in the fall when the apples and cranberries are fresh.

5	apples	5
1 cup	cranberries	250 mL
1/2 cup	brown sugar	125 mL
3 Tbsp	flour	45 mL
2 tsp	cinnamon	10 mL
4	egg whites	4
1/2 tsp	cream of tartar	2 mL
2/3 cup	white sugar	175 mL
1 tsp	vanilla	5 mL

Peel, core and chop the apples (about 6 cups/1.5 L chopped). Combine apples, cranberries, brown sugar, flour and cinnamon together. Spoon into 10 in/25 cm pie plate. Cover with tin foil and bake at 325°F for 20 minutes. This part can be made one day in advance and chilled. Bring to room temperature before proceeding.

Beat egg whites and cream of tartar together until soft peaks form. Gradually beat in white sugar to stiff peak stage. Fold in vanilla.

Cover fruit completely with meringue. Bake at 325°F for 35-40 minutes until golden brown. Serve immediately.

Serves 8.

Nutritional analysis per serving:
215 calories   2 g protein   1 g fat   54 g carbohydrate   0 mg cholesterol

BROWN RICE PUDDING
Ted Cohn

This low-fat version of traditional rice pudding is delicious. It can be made in a casserole dish instead of individual custard cups if you wish.

1 1/2 cups	skim milk	375 mL
1/2 cup	honey	125 mL
3	egg whites	3
2 tsp	vanilla	10 mL
1/2 tsp	cinnamon	2 mL
2 cups	cooked brown rice	500 mL
1/4 cup	raisins	50 mL
1/4 cup	dates, chopped	50 mL
	nutmeg	

Combine milk, honey, egg whites, vanilla and cinnamon. Beat with mixer until smooth. Stir in rice, raisins and dates. Spoon mixture into six custard cups. Sprinkle with nutmeg.

Place custard cups into a baking pan. Surround with hot water to a depth of 1 in/2.5 cm.

Bake at 325°F for 50 minutes or until set in the centre. Remove from baking pan and let cool.

Makes 6 servings.

Nutritional analysis per serving:
214 calories   6 g protein   1 g fat   48 g carbohydrate   1 mg cholesterol

Traditional custards are usually high in cholesterol and fat, but puddings made with low fat milk can be a sweet ending to a low fat meal.

ORANGE TAPIOCA PUDDING
Ruth Sanders

Ruth suggests to garnish this delightful pudding with mandarin orange sections or any of your favourite fruit combination. Add a dollop of light Cool Whip™ before serving, if you wish.

1/4 cup	**quick cooking tapioca**	**50 mL**
2 1/2 cups	**orange juice**	**625 mL**
2 Tbsp	**sugar or** **sugar substitute equivalent**	**30 mL**
1 tsp	**grated orange rind**	**5 mL**

Combine tapioca, orange juice and sugar and mix well. Heat until mixture comes to a boil and is thickened, stirring constantly (about 10 minutes). Stir in grated orange rind. Pour into serving bowl or individual dishes and cool. Garnish as desired.

If you are using Equal™ or aspartame as a sugar substitute, add it to the mixture **after** heating and mix well.

Serves 4.

Nutritional analysis per serving:
143 calories   1 g protein   0 g fat   36 g carbohydrate   0 mg cholesterol

Tapioca is made from the roots of the cassava plant. Quick cooking tapioca is the easiest to use – mix with low fat milk and cook according to package directions for a quick low fat dessert.

STRAWBERRY TOFU MOUSSE
Jean Wilder

This dessert looks especially elegant when served in wine glasses or small dessert dishes. Garnish with fresh mint leaves and sliced strawberries.

1/4 lb	soft tofu, drained	125 g
2 cups	strawberries, fresh or frozen	500 mL
2 small	bananas, ripe	2 small
1/2 tsp	nutmeg	2 mL
2 tsp	maple syrup	10 mL
	sliced strawberries for garnish	
	mint leaves for garnish	

In a blender or food processor, combine all ingredients except the garnishes. Puree thoroughly. Spoon into wine glasses and chill for 30 minutes before serving. Garnish.

Serves 4.

Nutritional analysis per serving:
105 calories   3 g protein   2 g fat   22 g carbohydrate   0 mg cholesterol

Eileen McIntosh suggests, you can mix together plain low fat yogurt and a package of lite hot chocolate. Let it sit in the refrigerator for at least 1/2 hour. It will make an easy dessert that tastes just like chocolate pudding.

4-3-2-1 Fruit Sherbet

Estelle Hagelund

A delicious refreshing frozen dessert that the whole family will love.

4	bananas, just ripe	4
3	oranges, medium	3
2	lemons	2
1 cup	sugar	250 mL

Mash bananas. Squeeze the juice from oranges and lemons. In a blender or food processor add bananas, orange juice, lemon juice, some of the fruit pulp and sugar. Blend until smooth.

Freeze in 8 individual serving dishes or 1 loaf pan. Take out of the freezer 5 minutes before serving.

Serves 8.

Nutritional analysis per serving:
170 calories   1 g protein   0 g fat   44 g carbohydrate   0 mg cholesterol

There are so many low fat frozen desserts now available. Try sherbets, ice milk, frozen yogurt, Gelato™ and Dole Whip™ instead of ice cream.

CRANBERRY PISTACHIO BISCOTTI
Shauna Ratner

These Italian biscuits are the "dunking" cookies of the 90's! Serve them with a cup of robust coffee or a dish of mouth puckering lemon sorbet.

1 1/3 cups	dried cranberries	375 mL
2 1/2 cups	flour	625 mL
1 cup	sugar	250 mL
1/2 tsp	baking soda	2 mL
1/2 tsp	baking powder	2 mL
3	eggs	3
1 tsp	vanilla	5 mL
3/4 cup	shelled pistachio nuts, halved	200 mL
1	egg white	1
1 tsp	water	5 mL

In a bowl combine the cranberries with enough hot water to cover and let soak for 5 minutes. Drain the cranberries well and pat them dry with paper towels. In mixing bowl combine flour, sugar, baking soda and baking powder. Add the eggs and vanilla beating until dough is formed. Stir in the cranberries and the pistachio nuts.

Turn the dough out onto a lightly floured surface. Knead several times and divide dough into two. Working on a large "buttered" and floured baking sheet, with floured hands, form each piece of dough into a flattish log 13 in/33 cm long and 2 in/5 cm wide. Arrange the logs at least 3 in/8 cm apart. Mix egg white and 1 tsp/5 mL water together and brush onto logs. Bake in the middle of oven at 325°F for 30 minutes. Let cool on baking rack for 10 minutes.

On a cutting board cut the logs crosswise on the diagonal into 1/2 in/1 cm slices. Arrange the biscotti cut side down on the baking sheet. Bake at 325°F for 10 – 12 minutes or until pale golden. Transfer onto baking racks and let cool. Store in airtight containers.

Makes 42 biscotti.

Nutritional analysis per biscotti:
74 calories   2 g protein   2 g fat   14 g carbohydrate   17 mg cholesterol

Almost anything can be added to biscotti to suit your taste. Add dry fruits, whole wheat flour, a touch of nuts or various spices such as crushed peppercorns, anise seed or ginger.

DATE SQUARES
Maria Ragone

Make these during the holiday season using President's Choice, "I Can't Believe It's Not Mincemeat – 5 Mixed Fruits Without Suet"™, in place of the date mixture.

2 cups	dates, chopped	500 mL
1 cup	water	250 mL
1 tsp	lemon rind, grated	5 mL
1 Tbsp	lemon juice	15 mL
1 1/4 cups	rolled oats	300 mL
1 cup	whole wheat flour	250 mL
1/2 tsp	baking powder	2 mL
1/2 cup	brown sugar	125 mL
1/3 cup	soft margarine	75 mL

Combine dates, water, lemon rind and lemon juice in a pot and bring to a boil. Simmer 5-10 minutes until soft and thick, stirring occasionally.

In a bowl, combine rolled oats, flour, baking powder and brown sugar. Rub in margarine until crumbly. Press one half of mixture into lightly greased 8 in/20 cm square pan. Spread with date filling. Press remaining crumb mixture lightly on top. Bake at 350°F for 35 minutes until lightly browned.

Makes 20 squares.

Nutritional analysis per square:
139 calories   2 g protein   4 g fat   27 g carbohydrate   0 mg cholesterol

CEREAL SQUARES

Cereals are not just a breakfast food. Snack on them as is, or use them for toppings on flavoured yogurt or make them into desserts such as crisps and crumbles.

LIGHT RICE KRISPIE™ SQUARES

4 Tbsp	margarine	60 mL
40	marshmallows	40
2 tsp	vanilla	10 mL
12 cups	Rice Krispies™	3 L

In large saucepan (preferably nonstick) melt margarine. Add marshmallows. Stir constantly over low heat until marshmallows are melted. Remove from heat. Add vanilla and mix well. Add Rice Krispies™ and stir until Rice Krispies™ are coated with marshmallow mixture. Press into an ungreased (10 x15 in/25 x 38 cm) plastic container. Cut into squares when cool.

Makes 24 squares.

Nutritional analysis per square:
112 calories   2 g protein   2 g fat   23 g carbohydrate   0 mg cholesterol

WHEAT OR RICE PUFF SQUARES

1/4 cup	soft margarine	50 mL
1/2 cup	corn syrup	125 mL
1 cup	brown sugar	250 mL
12 cups	puffed wheat or puffed rice	3 L
2 tsp	vanilla	10 mL

In a large pot, combine margarine, corn syrup and brown sugar. Boil 3-5 minutes until at hard-ball stage. Remove from heat. Mix in vanilla. Quickly add puffed wheat or rice and mix well. Press into two 9 x 9 in/23 x 23 cm pans.

Makes 24 squares.

Nutritional analysis per square:
97 calories   1 g protein   2 g fat   19 g carbohydrate   0 mg cholesterol

BAKED APPLES

These are especially good when topped with light whipped topping or vanilla flavoured yogurt.

4	apples	4
1/4 cup	raisins	50 mL
1/4 cup	nuts, chopped (optional)	50 mL
2 Tbsp	brown sugar	30 mL
1/2 tsp	cinnamon	2 mL
1/4 tsp	nutmeg	1 mL
1/3 cup	water	75 mL

Wash and core apples. Peel strip from top of each apple. Place apples in 8 cup/2 L baking dish. Combine raisins, nuts (if using), brown sugar, cinnamon and nutmeg. Spoon mixture into centres of apples. Pour water around each apple in dish.

Bake at 350°F for 40 – 45 minutes until apples are tender, basting occasionally with liquid. If microwaving, reduce water to 2 Tbsp/30 mL. Microwave covered on high for 4 – 8 minutes or until tender, rearranging and basting apples once.

Serves 4.

Nutritional analysis per apple:
178 calories   2 g protein   5 g fat   35 g carbohydrate   0 mg cholesterol

PASTRY

Yvonne Wallace

Traditional pie crust calls for 3/4 – 1 cup of shortening per double pie crust. This pastry has half of that fat, but will still give you a nice crust to use with your favourite filling.

1 3/4 cups	flour	450 mL
6 Tbsp	vegetable shortening	90 mL
1/4 tsp	baking powder	1 mL
1/3 cup	water	75 mL

In medium size mixing bowl mix the flour, shortening and baking powder. Work together with a pastry blender until crumbly. Add water and mix together with a fork. Use your hands to form a ball with the dough.

Lightly flour a surface and roll out the dough. Bake according to pie directions.

Makes 2 crusts.

Nutritional analysis per 1/8 pie (crust only):
163 calories   2 g protein   9 g fat   19 g carbohydrate   0 mg cholesterol

Half the crust is half the fat! Make a single crust pie and instead of the upper crust try a meringue topping or a crumb crust. Another alternative is to make a graham wafer or chocolate wafer crust for the bottom, and sprinkle a little of the cookie crumbs on top.

CREAMY RICE PUDDING
Estelle Hagelund

For a decadent dessert serve this with pureed frozen berries or sprinkle toasted almonds on top. Grated crushed candied ginger or raisins can also be added for a taste treat.

1/2 cup	short grain rice	125 mL
2 Tbsp	sugar	30 mL
2 1/3 cups	skim or 1% milk	575 mL
1 tsp	vanilla	5 mL

Cook rice, sugar and milk in double boiler until rice is tender. Remove from heat and let cool. Add vanilla.

Serves 4.

Nutritional analysis per serving (with skim milk):
161 calories   6 g protein   0 g fat   32 g carbohydrate   3 mg cholesterol

Pureed fruit sauces, also called "coulis" can be used in so many ways to brighten up an ordinary dessert in both flavour and colour. Try raspberry coulis in frozen yogurt or top crepes with a blackberry coulis.